GEOLOGY AND SCENERY IN THE LAKE DISTRICT

Other Macmillan titles of related interest

D. V. Ager, *The Nature of the Stratigraphical Record*
D. L. Dineley, *Aspects of a Stratigraphic System: The Devonian*
J. R. Haynes, *Foraminifera*
C. S. Hutchison, *Economic Deposits and their Tectonic Setting*
F. Moseley, *The Volcanic Rocks of the Lake District*
H. H. Read and Janet Wilson, *Introduction to Geology:*
                                 Volume 1 Principles
                                 Volume 2 Earth History,
                                    Part 1: Early Stages of Earth History
                                 Volume 2 Earth History,
                                    Part 2: Later Stages of Earth History

Front cover: Honister Crag

Geology and Scenery in the Lake District

F. MOSELEY
Reader in Geology,
Department of Geological Sciences,
University of Birmingham

MACMILLAN

First published 1986

Published by
MACMILLAN EDUCATION LTD
Houndmills, Basingstoke, Hampshire RG21 2XS
and London
Companies and representatives
throughout the world

Typeset by TecSet Ltd,
Sutton, Surrey

Printed in Hong Kong

British Library Cataloguing in Publication Data
Moseley, F.
    Geology and scenery in the Lake District.
    1. Geology—England—Lake District
    I. Title
    554.27′8   QE262.L2

ISBN 0-333-41781-X

Contents

Preface

This book follows on from *The Volcanic Rocks of the Lake District* (Moseley, 1983a) in which the environment of the 450 million year old 'Borrowdale Volcano' was described, and a number of field excursions detailed. It is, like the first book, mostly concerned with the volcanic rocks which form the central core of Lakeland, but it also includes sections on the older Skiddaw Slates and the younger Silurian and Carboniferous rocks. The method adopted has been to use numerous illustrations, the written sections being kept to a minimum. I hope the book will prove to be understandable to amateur geologists and to those just beginning to study the subject; nevertheless, there should be sufficient information for professionals not familiar with the Lake District and for those wishing to lead University parties across the ground.

Although the two books together contain 30 excursion guides and recommendations, they by no means exhaust the possibilities for the Lake District. These guides deal only with the areas I know best, and important and popular regions such as Scafell, Skiddaw and Haweswater have not yet been covered.

Note on maps

Maps given in this book show the general route of each excursion. It is recommended that these be supplemented by the appropriate walkers' maps for the area. The whole of the Lake District is covered by an Ordnance Survey 1:50 000 (about $1\frac{1}{4}$ inches to 1 mile) Tourist Map. Even better are the 1:25 000 (about $2\frac{1}{2}$ inches to 1 mile) Ordnance Survey series. The relevant maps are noted at the beginning of each excursion. Four 'Outdoor Leisure' maps are also available which cover the whole of the Lake District at a scale of 1:25 000. All these maps are obtainable from local Ordnance Survey stockists.

1

Introduction

Those of us who spend a lifetime in one career are so familiar with the subject matter that it becomes easy to assume that most people are acquainted with at least some of the fundamentals. This is not necessarily so, however, and many who are expert in their own field can easily think that other disciplines are too specialised for their attention, that the subject matter may not interest them, or that there is little time in a busy life to master the details. As far as geology is concerned I am convinced that those who enjoy scenery will be interested in geological explanations, provided that they are kept simple and not confused by unnecessary jargon. I aim therefore to interpret the geological landscape of the Lake District so that those physically active members of our community who derive pleasure from fell walking will gain the added interest of knowing something of the ways in which the mountains were formed. I like to know something of the plants I see around me, although I am no botanist, and I also pay attention to human history and to the Lakeland poets. Equally I think the history

of the rocks which form a framework to our landscape will be of interest to non-geologists.

The Lake District may have a quieter landscape than more exotic places elsewhere, but I think the beauty of the scenery can compete with that of any part of the world. Much of the geology is more subtle than that of some deserts where the rocks are not concealed by vegetation, or parts of Greenland where bare stark mountains rise above glaciers, but I hope this book will show how rock formations can be seen on the fellsides and crags and their fundamental nature appreciated. The Lake District contains a wide variety of both scenery and geology within a compact area. Yosemite in California is a beautiful region but the National Park, much larger than the Lake District, is composed almost entirely of granite. In the Alps the Matterhorn has varied geology, but not all tourists will feel inclined to ascend the precipices to inspect it. The Lake District is both varied and accessible, and because of the deep erosion of the valleys by ice-age glaciers the mountains seem to be much higher than

they really are. Indeed, looking at misty Scafell from Hard Knott on one occasion, it was difficult to convince a foreign visitor that an overnight stop at an intermediate hut was not necessary for its ascent.

We must all hope to attract others to share and appreciate the beauty of the Lake District, but at the same time we must persuade them not to damage the environment. Geological conservation is in the interests of us all, whether we are research workers, students in field parties or tourists on holiday, and I sincerely hope that the simple code of behaviour indicated below will be followed.

First is the plea to avoid the indiscriminate use of geological hammers. Large and apparently enthusiastic parties can wreak havoc on first-rate exposures so that they not only become ugly scars but the beautiful structures once displayed are destroyed forever. The sharp slivers of rock then scattered around can become a danger to sheep. It is apparent that most of those who break off pieces of rock do not require them for future research work or

even for their garden rockery, and it is nearly always possible to obtain perfectly satisfactory specimens from weathered material below an outcrop. The emphasis must be — *please do not hammer rocks unnecessarily*. Indeed the use of a hand lens on a weathered surface nearly always gives more information than a broken piece of rock, something I learned long ago from that maestro of Lake District geology, 'Mick' Mitchell.

The second point is that Lakeland farmers must get sick and tired of tourists, geologists or otherwise, who leave gates open or climb over them and break the hinges, or climb walls and fences regardless of damage, and seem to think it is their right to do so. Geological parties sometimes carry more blame in this respect than ordinary walkers, since the best rock exposures do not always lie close to 'rights of way'. This leads me to footpaths. The geology is commonly investigated well away from footpaths, the geologist crossing boggy moorland and rough crags to inspect isolated exposures. This is as it should be, but there are occasions when footpaths form the best excursion route, as for example when examining the tuffs of

Figure 1 **Danger on the Mountains. A chance meeting with *Buttermeresaurus crossi* on the High Stile Range could certainly prove hazardous, but there are other more immediate dangers. The weather can change from a mild sunny day to a howling blizzard within the space of half an hour. All walkers should be prepared with extra warm clothing, wind and waterproofs, adequate footwear and extra nutritious food. It is very easy to get lost; the bright sunshine with the lake in the distance is replaced by swirling mist. Never go amongst the mountains without those most valuable items, a large-scale map and a compass, and know how to use them. It is equally easy to damage yourself, so take a first-aid kit**

Bowfell, or Helm Crag, Grasmere, or descending to Langdale from Stickle Tarn. In such cases, please follow the designated path even though it zigs and zags and may be considerably longer than the direct route down the fellside. Short cuts are not really a demonstration of superior manhood, and boots can disturb a delicate vegetation balance and initiate erosion, which is difficult to control.

It is not possible to discuss the preservation of our countryside without mentioning rubbish. The sordid remains of the contents of lunch boxes should be taken off the mountains and disposed of in litter bins. Certainly they should not be thrown behind the nearest rock, a common British habit, nor should they be buried using that most versatile of tools, the geological hammer. Cans remain forever and sooner or later may do serious damage to sheep. The instruction is — *please take it off the fells.*

My final point is concerned with safety on the mountains. Even small ones like those of the Lake District are dangerous places. The caption to figure 1 indicates some of the hazards waiting for the unwary, and it has to be stressed that Lake District Mountain Rescue teams turn out many times each year in horrific conditions to rescue the stupid; for example: 'three walkers lost near Scafell on March 7th, blizzard conditions, discovered wearing shorts, no spare food, no maps, near to death.' It is essential to be properly equipped, and to remember that conditions can change from mild weather to a winter blizzard in half an hour. This sort of advice will be common sense to experienced fell walkers, but does not appear to be so to those new to the mountains. It will apply to geological parties, school or university, and leaders should ensure that all their members are properly equipped. Boots, waterproof and windproof clothing, spare pullovers and other clothes in plastic bags (in a rucksack), spare high-calorie food, and a first-aid kit, should all be carried. After one harrowing experience when a student collapsed with hypothermia on a mild but wet November day, I will not allow anyone in my parties to wear jeans, unless the wearers have waterproof gear in their rucksacks.

Having stressed care on the mountains, I nevertheless do not wish to push the matter too far. Geologists engaged in projects generally have to work alone and the important requirements in these circumstances are to be properly equipped, and to leave an indication of the route for the day at lodgings, pinned to the tent or with the car.

I will now consider briefly the geological outline of the Lake District illustrated by figures 2, 3 and 4. The main part of the region is made up of three thick rock units of Lower Palaeozoic age (Ordovician and Silurian). The oldest rocks are the Skiddaw Slates which form the rounded mountains of the northern fells. They are overlain by some 5000 metres of volcanic rocks, the Borrowdale Volcanics, which form the crags of central Lakeland, and these are in turn overlain by thick sequences, predominantly of mudstones and sandstones, which form the lower hills in the south (the Windermere Group, extending from the Upper Ordovician to the top of the Silurian). Peripheral to the Lake District are younger rocks of Carboniferous and Permo-Triassic age, including the Carboniferous Limestone which forms prominent escarpments around the rim of the Lake District. The present landscape owes its character partly to these rocks and partly to the sculpturing by Quaternary ice-age glaciers.

Let us now look at the major geological divisions of the Lake District in a little more detail, starting with the oldest rocks, the Skiddaw Slates. From the outset it has to be said that they are difficult rocks to understand, in my opinion one of the most difficult groups in Britain, and really the province of the specialist. It is nevertheless easy to appreciate that mountains such as Skiddaw and the hills around Loweswater are made of softish rocks of uniform hardness, simply because of the smooth fellsides and the absence of distinguishing features, even though this is a negative approach to rock identification and interpretation. A distant view of a Skiddaw Slate mountain reveals little of the geological structure and the true nature of the rock is only revealed by close inspection (figures 7 and 8). Even then, not every outcrop can be readily interpreted and there have been many unresolved discussions and arguments about them. The Skiddaw Slates are indeed difficult rocks, fascinating to the expert in structural geology or palaeontology, but since this book is not primarily intended for such folk these rocks have been treated only briefly herein.

The Borrowdale Volcanics are an entirely different proposition, and, whilst the details require specialist attention, the broad generalities of many exposures can be appreciated by all once they are pointed out. They also form the craggy summits of the most popular walking areas from Scafell to Coniston, to

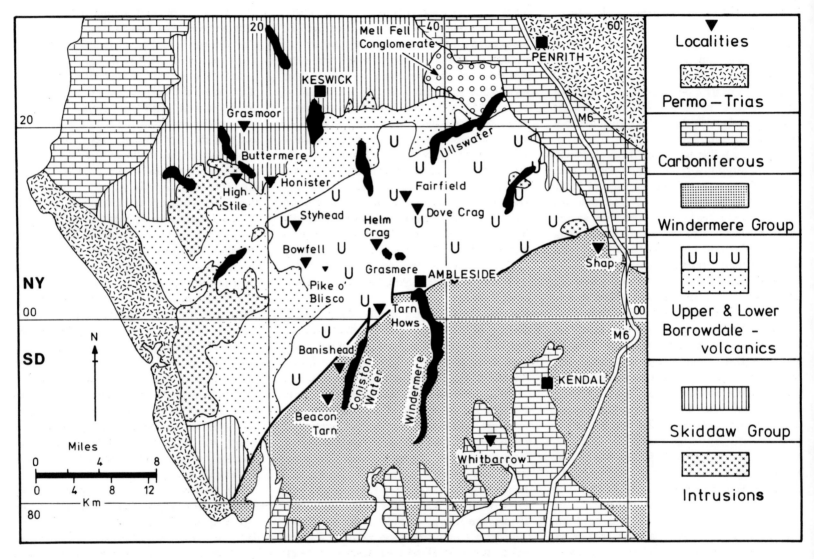

Figure 2 A geological map of the Lake District showing the locations of the areas described. The Windermere Group includes all the Upper Ordovician and Silurian sedimentary rocks above the Borrowdale Volcanics (Moseley, 1984)

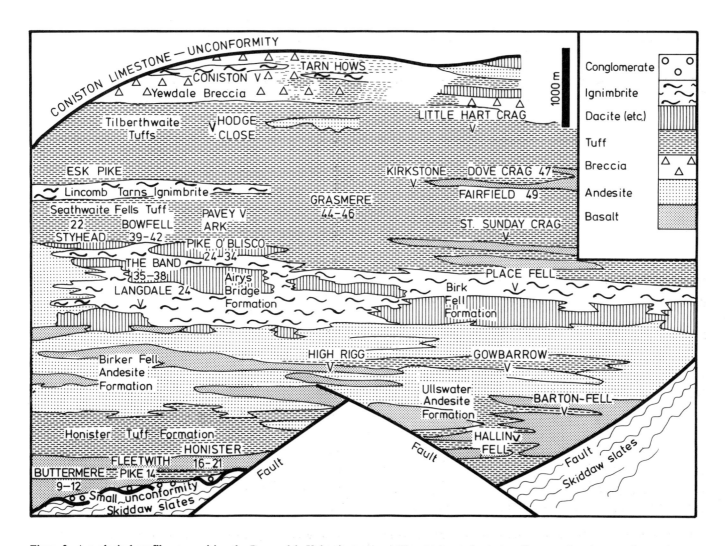

Figure 3 A geological profile summarising the Borrowdale Volcanic sequence. The numbers refer to text figures and to the excursions which have been described, and show the relative positions within the Borrowdale Volcano of the local volcanic sequences. The letter V refers to the locations of excursions described in *The Volcanic Rocks of the Lake District* (Moseley, 1983a). The division between the lower and upper volcanics (figure 2) is between the andesites and basalts of the Birker Fell and Ullswater Formations and the ignimbrites and dacites of the Airy's Bridge Formation and its correlatives

5

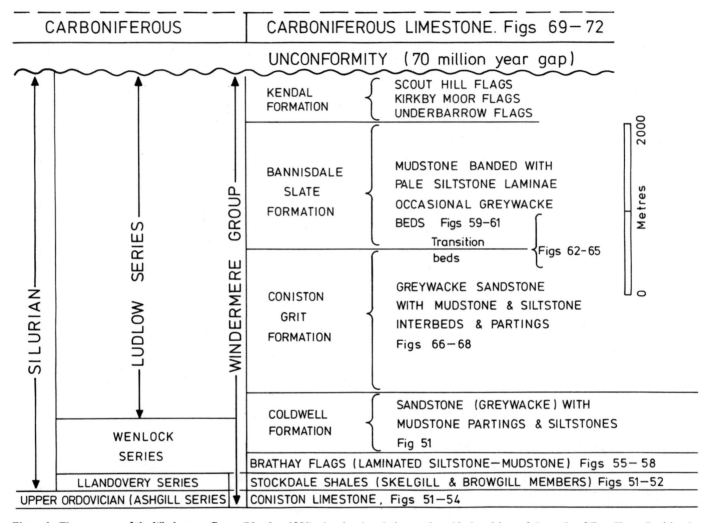

Figure 4 The sequence of the Windermere Group (Moseley, 1984), showing the relative stratigraphical positions of the rocks of Tarn Hows, Banishead, Beacon Tarn and Shap (figures 51 to 68)

Helvellyn and High Street and I therefore devote more space to them than to the other rocks. The Borrowdale Volcanics are the eroded remnant of an ancient Ordovician volcano which must at one time have stood more than 5000 metres high. This was about 450 million years ago when the Lake District lay 20° south of the equator (Faller and Briden, 1978; Moseley, 1983a), and the oceans and continents were distributed differently from those of the present day. Since then earth movements, mountain building and erosion have greatly modified the structure and landforms of the district, which adds to the difficulties of interpretation.

The complex sequence of lava and ash of the volcano was built up over a period of perhaps 10 million years, and since these rocks were subsequently tilted, folded and eroded, different levels of the volcano can be inspected at different locations. Figure 3 shows the reconstructed volcanic sequence and the positions in the sequence of excursion areas described later in the book. The principal rocks to be seen are lavas and ashes or tuff. The lavas include basalts, which are generally dark in colour and so fine grained that it is difficult to pick out constituent crystals, andesites, the most common of the lavas, which are generally medium grey, and dacites and rhyolites, which are usually pale grey, weathering to white. The tuffs may be coarse grained where they are formed of large angular fragments blown out of the volcano by violent explosions, or bedded (layered) where the ash has fallen into water and been reworked by currents. One of the most spectacular tuffs is ignimbrite, formed by blasts of incandescent ash, the modern examples of which have been the most destructive type of volcanic explosion known. All these rocks are described in more detail under the excursions and in Moseley (1983a); see also Moseley and Millward (1982).

The rocks of the Windermere Group (Moseley, 1984 and figure 4) in contrast with the volcanics, consist of sedimentary rocks deposited in seas of varying depth. These rocks form the beautifully wooded, gently undulating landscape of the southern Lake District, and make excellent walking country rather than the energetic climbing terrains of the volcanic mountains.

Deposition of the Windermere Group sediments was followed, at the end of the Silurian Period, by the Caledonian mountain building (orogeny), during which time all the rocks described above were severely folded, fractured (faulted), and raised up to form the Caledonian mountains. This time was also important for the intrusion of a number of large igneous bodies, particularly the Shap and Skiddaw Granites. There had also been similar intrusions during Ordovician times such as the Ennerdale Granophyre and Eskdale Granite. They are all important elements of the scenery (Firman, 1978; Moseley, 1983a). Erosion subsequently reduced the Caledonian mountains and, after an interval of some 70 million years, the tropical Carboniferous seas advanced on to the Lake District, and the Carboniferous Limestones were deposited (figures 69 to 72).

We must not of course forget the effects of the last ice age, less than 1 million years ago, when glaciers gouged deeply into the rocks and left behind the impressive landscape which we see today. I realise that when describing the Lakeland scenery and geology, I have not done justice to the effects of the Quaternary Glaciation; nearly all the localities described in this book owe something to the erosional effects of the Quaternary glaciers.

Figure 5   Grasmoor from Gasgale Crags, Whiteside

8

2

The Skiddaw Slates of Whiteside, Gasgale and Grasmoor (1:25 000 map NY12)

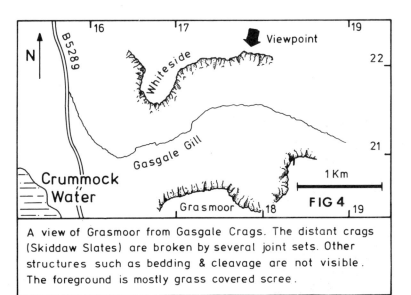

A view of Grasmoor from Gasgale Crags. The distant crags (Skiddaw Slates) are broken by several joint sets. Other structures such as bedding & cleavage are not visible. The foreground is mostly grass covered scree.

Figure 6   View of Grasmoor from Gasgale Crags (see figure 5)

The Skiddaw Slates are the oldest rocks in the Lake District and form the smooth rounded hills of the north. They contrast strongly with the sharp crags of the Borrowdale Volcanics further south, although there are exceptions, for example the steep crags of Saddleback and Grasmoor.

However, since they were formerly muds and sands they are understandably more easily weathered and eroded than the volcanic rocks.

The Skiddaw Slates were deposited in Ordovician times, about 450 million years ago, in moderately deep water on the continental slope of a former continent. The sediments were brought into this sub-marine environment by strong, fast turbidity currents made more dense than the surrounding water by the mud, sand and silt contained within them. Many different sedimentary structures resulted from this type of deposition and the slumping of wet sediment down sub-marine slopes to form sedimentary folds is perhaps the most common. Descriptions of these structures will be found in books specialising in sedimentology. The soft sediments were subsequently subjected to the high stresses of the Caledonian mountain building which crumpled them into complex small-scale tectonic folds and converted them to slate.

To casual observation much of the lithology is uniform and dull. The small folds are only recognised where exposure is good, and the beginner will undoubtedly gaze at many Skiddaw Slate outcrops with little understanding. It is difficult to pick out important structures in distant views, which is not the case with the harder volcanics where lava flows, for example, make strong features. On the crags of Grasmoor (figures 5 and 6) the only structures to be seen from the opposite side of the valley are a few small faults and master joints, even though the rocks are folded in a style just as complex as that shown on figure 7.

There are numerous small folds on Gasgale Crags such as those shown

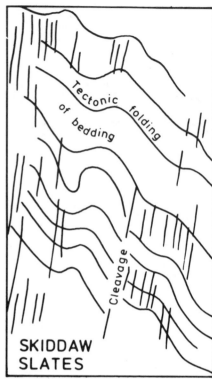

SKIDDAW SLATES

Soft mudstones deformed into small scale folds & cleaved (see text) during the Caledonian mountain building (Orogeny)

Figure 7   Minor folds and cleavage in Skiddaw mudstones of Gasgale Crags

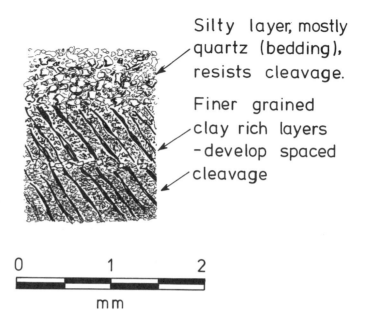

Silty layer, mostly quartz (bedding), resists cleavage.

Finer grained clay rich layers - develop spaced cleavage

0   1   2

mm

Figure 8 Enlargement showing bedding and cleavage in Skiddaw mudstone, Gasgale

in figure 7 in mudstones of the Kirkstile Slate Formation. The folds are cut by a cleavage which roughly bisects the angle between the fold limbs, and is therefore sub-parallel to the axial planes of the folds. It will be noticed that the cleavage is more pronounced in the finer-grained layers which were more easily deformed by the stresses (figure 8). Flaky phyllosilicate materials (mica and clay minerals which occur as thin flakes only visible under the high power of a microscope) are abundant in fine-grained muds and were recrystallised by stress during the Caledonian mountain building to lie at right angles to that compression. The coarser-grained layers consist mostly of quartz which offered more resistance to recrystallisation.

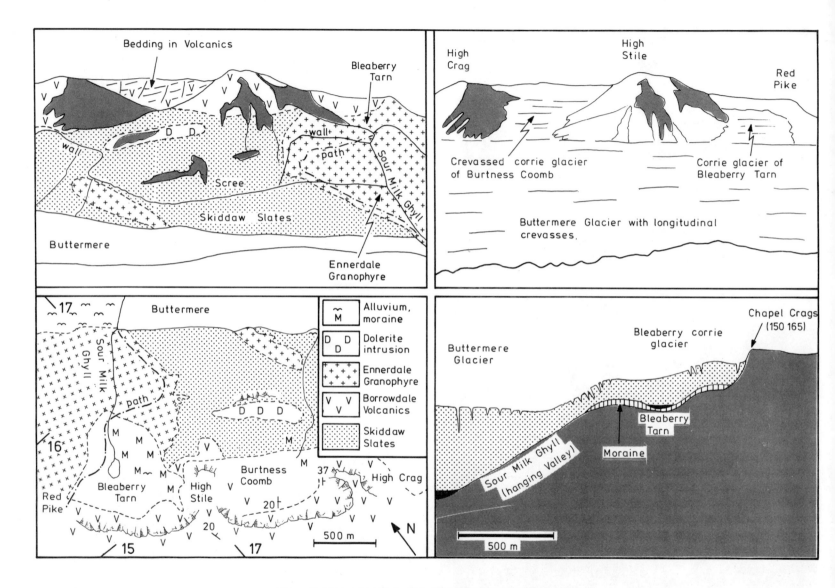

Figure 9 Map and sections of the High Stile Range and Buttermere

3

Glacial and Solid Geology of the Buttermere Area (1:25 000 map NY11)

The view of Buttermere and the High Stile Range from High Snockrigg is quite magnificent and enables one to pick out many details of both the glacial geology and the solid rocks. It is not an arduous climb from Newlands Pass at 340 metres to High Snockrigg at 530 metres (NY 187 169), and it is an advantage to go on a clear day armed with binoculars when all the details of the topography can be picked out (figures 10, 11 and 12).

Let us consider the glacial geology first. The erosion which deepened the Lakeland valleys and moulded the numerous rock outcrops to their present form has long been established as largely of glacial origin. These events occurred more than 20 000 years ago when the Lake District, Scotland and North Wales resembled present-day Greenland.

The greater part of erosion in glaciated mountains is accomplished by large valley glaciers, such as those descending to the Denmark Strait in East Greenland. Simultaneously small tributary glaciers, or corrie glaciers, enter the main glacier from the side and, being less powerful than the main glacier, are unable to erode so deeply and thus emerge on to the valley side as hanging valleys, of which Sour Milk Ghyll is a prime example. There are usually ice falls and crevasses in areas like this. The corrie glaciers also cut back deeply into the mountain ridges leaving steep cliffs. When they melt they may deposit moraine on the corrie lip and leave a small lake (corrie, cwm, combe, tarn), as seen on figure 13.

The solid rocks were described in a field excursion guide by Moseley (1983a). The drawing (figure 11) can be compared with the map (figure 9) and, taken together, these should be self-explanatory. In outline, a walk up the steep footpath from the western end of Buttermere to Bleaberry Tarn and Red Pike will reveal several rock types. First the Ennerdale Granophyre is encountered, outcropping on both sides of the path, here very close to its junction with the Skiddaw Slates (Firman, 1978). It is a pink microgranite in which the crystals of quartz and feldspar are clearly visible. At the top of the steep part of the path the Bleaberry Tarn moraine is well seen, and at the top of Red Pike the granophyre is encountered again. There is an exhilarating walk along Chapel Crags to High Stile, with lava flows, bedded tuffs and agglomerate revealed in the crags and, a little south of High Stile summit, an excellent low outcrop of 'bird's eye' tuff (Moseley, 1983a) which I saw for the first time during November 1983. Further along the ridge Burtness Combe is impressive seen from above, and a descent can be made here to examine the dolerite and Skiddaw Slates. *But please note that this descent is only for experienced fell walkers*, and then preferably not in cloud. The alternative route is to descend to Scarth Gap and Buttermere.

The return to Buttermere village can be via Gatesgarth and the road, or along the attractive south shore to the starting point.

Figure 10   High Stile and Buttermere 20 000 years ago. The Ice Age. Burtness Combe and Bleaberry Tarn are shown as tributary corrie glaciers

Figure 11   The High Stile Range from High Snockrigg. Compare with figure 9

Figure 12   High Stile from the east. In some cases Borrowdale Volcanic structures are obvious, for example see figures 16, 22, 44 etc., but in others they are not. In this diagram, individual lavas cannot be picked out and the visible structural lines are all joints

Figure 13   Bleaberry Tarn and Buttermere from Red Pike (see figure 9). Note the hummocky moraine which has formed on the corrie lip

Figure 14   Fleetwith Pike and Warnscale Bottom from the ENE

4

The Borrowdale Volcanics of Fleetwith Pike and Honister (1:25 000 map NY21)

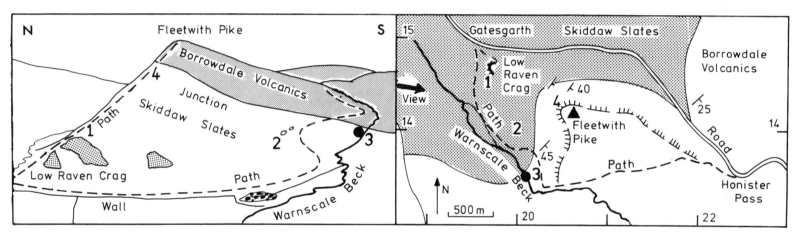

Figure 15   Diagram and map to show the geology of Fleetwith Pike and Warnscale

FLEETWITH PIKE

The view of Fleetwith Pike shown on figure 14 is impressive both scenically and geologically. The upper parts of the pike and the steeper slopes of Warnscale Beck are composed of hard volcanic rocks which form steep crags and es-carpments so that the base of the volcanics can be easily traced from Fleetwith Edge to Warnscale Beck. The volcanic rocks are mostly lava flows with subsidiary tuffs, the lavas becoming dominant in the lower part of the sequence. The lavas, which are usually between 15 and 30 metres thick, are partly basalt and basaltic andesite, and partly andesite, and were described in outline by Moseley (1983a). Details of some of the andesite lavas are illustrated in figure 20. The whole of this part of the succession is in-clined at about 25° to the south-east, as shown on figure 15, and this can be seen from the way in which the base of the volcanics outcrops high

Figure 16 The north side of Honister Pass. Old workings in the tuffs (slates)

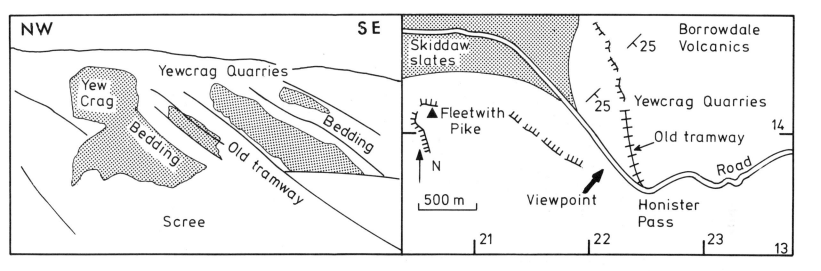

Figure 17 Diagram and map of north Honister. Tuffs (slates) dip to the south-east

on Fleetwith Edge and bends downwards into Warnscale. Skiddaw Slates occur below the volcanics and underlie the Buttermere area. They are softer rocks and more easily eroded, forming relatively smooth vegetation-covered slopes. Junctions between Skiddaw Slates and volcanics can be inspected in Warnscale Beck (locality 3) and on Fleetwith Edge (locality 4). An excursion guide incorporating these localities will be found in Moseley (1983a, chapter 6A). Although the Skiddaw Slate slopes appear from a distance to be largely unexposed, close inspection reveals that there are many small outcrops. The slates are folded in a complex way, rather like those of figure 7, but the uniform lithology often makes it difficult to see the structures. Near the bottom of Fleetwith Edge, a steeper outcrop, Low Raven Crag, is part of the Loweswater Flags

Formation. Here a hard greywacke sandstone interbedded with Skiddaw Slates (turbidite, see figure 64), stands out as a crag because of its greater hardness. There are complex structures in all these outcrops which experienced professional geologists in fact find it difficult to interpret. The remaining feature of interest shown by figure 14 is the flat area of Warnscale Bottom. This area was formerly part of Buttermere, but has gradually been silted up by fine-grained sediment brought down by streams, so that it is now an alluvial flat. Buttermere grows smaller each year from continuous sedimentation.

HONISTER

Honister Pass (figures 16 and 17) is well known to motorists as one of the steepest gradients in

Britain, and Honister Crag (figures 18 and 19) as one of the most impressive precipices in the Lake District (see front cover). Geologically and commercially it is best known for the ornamental slates worked in mines and quarries on both sides of the pass. The slate has been used as a facing stone on buildings in many parts of Britain and other parts of the world, and should one wish for a slate table, slate fireplace, or a base for a table lamp it is well worth a stop at the works on Honister Pass.

The slates originated as volcanic ash blown high into the atmosphere by titanic explosions. It would have drifted in the wind after the fashion of the ash from the 1980 Mount St. Helens eruption in North America and then fallen to mantle the landscape, perhaps many miles from the eruptive centre. Most of the ash settled

Figure 18 South Honister and Honister Crag

in shallow water, perhaps brought into lakes by rivers and then completely reworked by currents. This accounts for the banded patterns of coarser and finer fragments and the greens and greys of slightly different compositions which, when polished, make such an attractive ornamental stone (see figure 34). The ash is now consolidated into hard rock and can be referred to as 'tuff' or more correctly in modern parlance as 'volcaniclastic sandstone and siltstone'. Some beds of tuff are very attractive and others are less so. There are in fact two beds in the Honister area which are of particular value, known locally as the Honister and Kimberley 'veins'.

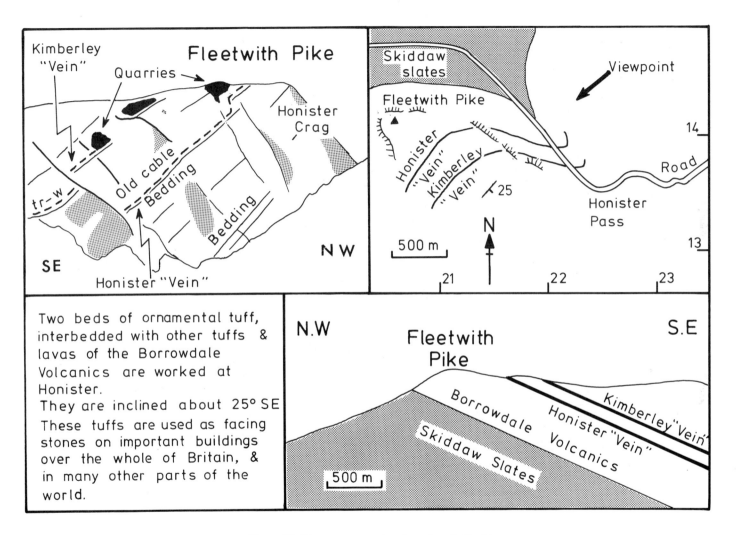

Two beds of ornamental tuff, interbedded with other tuffs & lavas of the Borrowdale Volcanics are worked at Honister.

They are inclined about 25° SE

These tuffs are used as facing stones on important buildings over the whole of Britain, & in many other parts of the world.

Figure 19 Diagram, map and section of south Honister

23

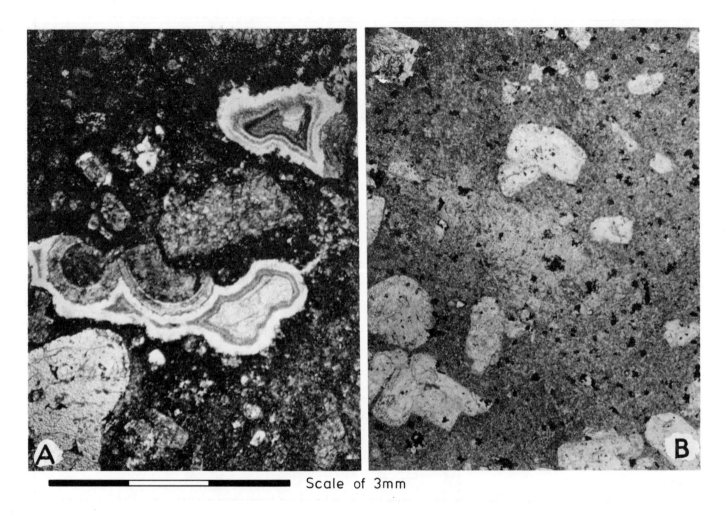

Scale of 3mm

Figure 20   Amygdaloidal and porphyritic andesite lava from the Honister sequence

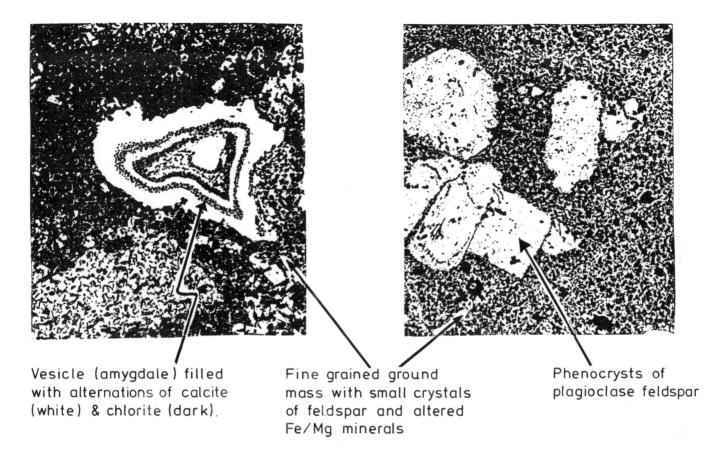

Vesicle (amygdale) filled
with alternations of calcite
(white) & chlorite (dark).

Fine grained ground
mass with small crystals
of feldspar and altered
Fe/Mg minerals

Phenocrysts of
plagioclase feldspar

Figure 21   Explanation of figure 20

ANDESITE LAVA FROM THE HONISTER
SEQUENCE (figures 20 and 21)

A. *Amygdaloidal andesite*. Lavas tend to gen-
erate volatiles which rise towards the surface
but may become trapped as gas bubbles by co-
agulation of the highly viscous magma. This is
referred to as a *vesicular texture*. Subsequently
circulating fluids may fill these vesicles and
minerals may be precipitated in them; this is
amygdaloidal texture. In this case the vesicles
have been filled by the minerals calcite (pale)
and chlorite (dark). The remainder of the rock
is highly decomposed with altered feldspar
phenocrysts (see B) and a fine-grained matrix.
B. *Porphyritic andesite*. This rock consists of
small (1 millimetre) phenocrysts (larger crystals
of which can be seen in hand specimens) of feldspar set in a much finer-grained matrix. This is
a porphyritic texture. The feldspar, which is the
most common of all minerals found in igneous
rocks, is in this case quite fresh and euhedral, in
that it shows natural crystal shapes indicating
that it crystallised in the still liquid magma. The
matrix consists of a scatter of black material,
most of which is opaque and difficult to identify, and a fine-grained mosaic of altered
feldspar and chlorite.

25

Figure 22   View from Green Gable to Styhead Tarn and Allen Crags

5

Styhead to Allen Crags (1:25 000 map NY20)

The view from Green Gable shown on figure 22 illustrates well the gently dipping formations of the Seathwaite Fells Tuffs and Lincomb Tarns Ignimbrite, well exposed around Styhead, Sprinkling Tarn and Allen Crags. The distance from Styhead to Allen Crags is 2 kilometres and the vertical height 340 metres. This is a popular walking area, with the principal footpath running from Styhead via Sprinkling Tarn, Angle Tarn and Rossett Ghyll into Langdale. The region was geologically described by Oliver (1961) who introduced all the rock names used here. Near Styhead Tarn the highest members of the Airy's Bridge Formation are acid lavas (dacites) and ignimbrites (figures 37 and 38). The Seathwaite Fells Tuffs rest on these rocks with a sharp junction which can be followed around Scafell and Bowfell and into Langdale where it traverses the higher parts of the Langdale Pikes (Moseley, 1983a, page 80). They were originally airfall tuffs, but of variable grain size according to the power of the eruption, and like the Honister tuffs were eventually deposited in water and reworked by currents.

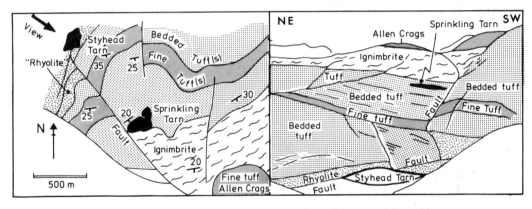

Figure 23 Map and diagram to show the geology of the area of figure 22

They are correctly called volcaniclastic sandstones, siltstones and mudstones (see figures 31 to 34). The depositional layers show up clearly from a distance, and close-up views of fresh surfaces reveal banding in different colours which make them valuable as ornamental stone where the outcrops are near main roads. Although they resemble the tuffs of Honister, these rocks formed much later in the history of the volcano and are some 2000 metres higher in the volcanic succession (figure 3).

The Lincomb Tarns Ignimbrite above the Seathwaite Fells Tuff was formed as a series of incandescent blasts. Eruptions of this type are described later in the book and the reader is referred to figures 37 and 38.

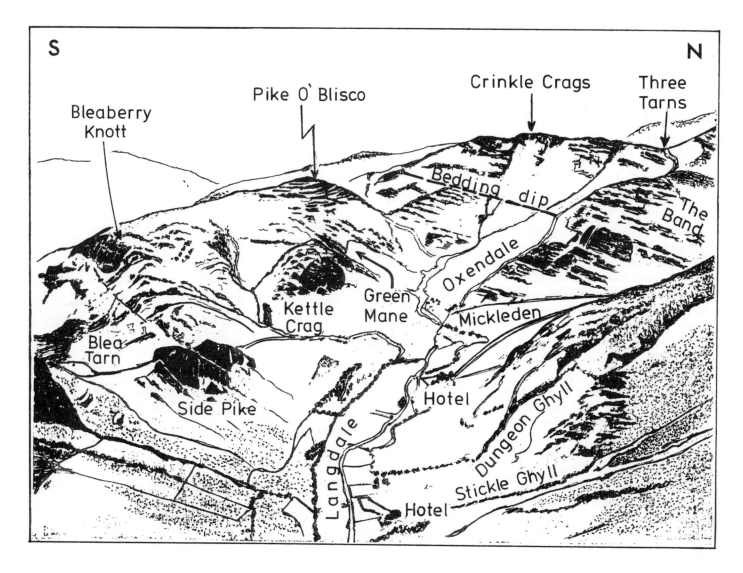

Figure 24   Aerial oblique of upper Langdale showing locations of figures 25 to 39

6

Pike o' Blisco, Langdale (1:25 000 map NY20)

The introductory aerial view (figure 24) is a panorama which shows the locations of most of the diagrams of figures 25 to 39. It also reveals the general geological structure and the relation between one area and another in a way that close-up inspection of the rocks fails to do – a clear advantage to any geological interpretation. It is often the case that an aerial view of a region makes it easier to see the overall geological structure whereas an observer on the ground, surrounded by numerous irregularly shaped crags, can easily become confused. In terrains such as the Lake District it is often a question of 'not being able to see the wood for the trees', and I can think of a number of areas where the geology is obvious on aerial photographs but difficult to comprehend on the ground. On figure 24 the layers of rock can be seen to be inclined from left to right, that is towards the NNE at about 15° to 20°. The rock units include dacite lavas and ignimbrites of the Airy's Bridge Formation, which form Crinkle Crags, the Band and much of Pike o'Blisco. There are also tuffs on Pike o'Blisco which are similar to those already described from the Honister region.

Figure 25   Pike o'Blisco from the Old Dungeon Ghyll Hotel

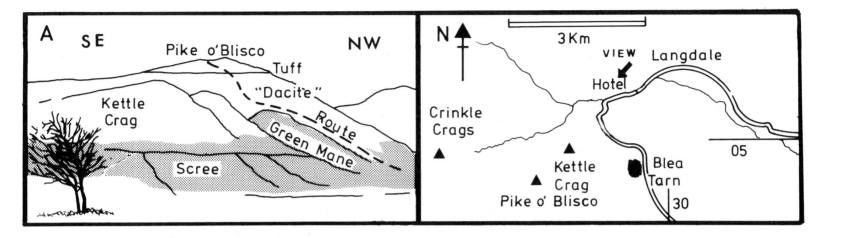

Figure 26   Explanatory map and sketch of figure 25

PIKE O'BLISCO

Most visitors to Langdale will usually give Pike o'Blisco a passing glance or they may fail to notice it at all. The Langdale Pikes, Crinkle Crags and Bowfell command the attention. However Pike o'Blisco is well worth consideration, both as an attractive walk with exquisite views and for its most interesting volcanic geology. The view from the Old Dungeon Ghyll Hotel (NY 286 061) reveals an outline of the geology, especially if binoculars are used. The upper parts of the Pike can be seen to be formed of layers which are inclined gently to the east (figures 25, 27 and 29). Lower down the fell the geological structure is less apparent, and Kettle Crag in the foreground remains a mystery from this viewpoint. For those who walk along Mickleden there are changing views of Pike o'Blisco including that of figure 29. The true nature of the rocks naturally cannot be seen without climbing the mountain. The route indicated here follows the footpath from Stool End towards Brown Ghyll until the footbridge is reached in Oxendale (NY 272 053). Exposures of dacite lava are seen hereabouts (figure 43). It is then necessary to leave the footpath and head directly up the hillside alongside the 'Green Mane'. This is an unusual feature as seen from the distance: a smooth green cone descending the rocky hillside between irregular craggy slopes. It is an ancient scree or alluvial cone now completely covered by vegetation, but I have not any particular view to offer about its origin. There are numerous outcrops along this route, all of dacite lava, some of which are flow-banded with gentle dips towards the east. Some distance above the Green Mane (figure 25) there are good exposures of bedded tuff, but if the route shown on figure 28 is followed one soon comes back on to dacite lava at B. This is because a fault has displaced the strata upwards towards the west. Eventually the top of the dacite is reached again at C, where it forms a strong bench with the bedded tuff (figure 33) rising steeply above. Traversing to the south-east one soon reaches the main footpath and the excursion route that I have described previously (Moseley, 1983a). From here to the summit there is a sequence of bedded tuffs with coarse tuff (figure 31), and then a strange breccia made up of angular and apparently welded blocks in the summit area.

Figure 27   An enlargement of figure 25, Pike o'Blisco summit

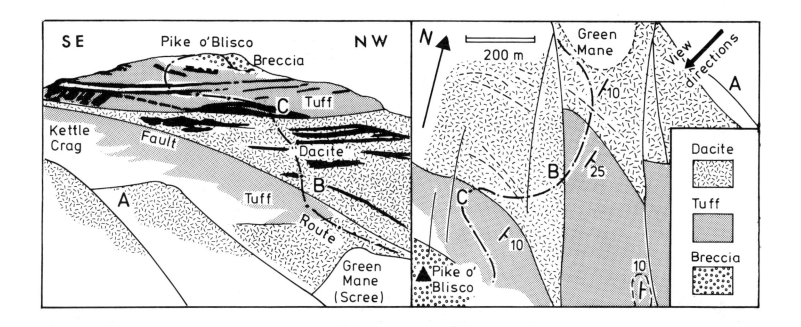

Figure 28   Detailed map and sketch of figure 27

Figure 29   Pike o'Blisco summit from Mickleden

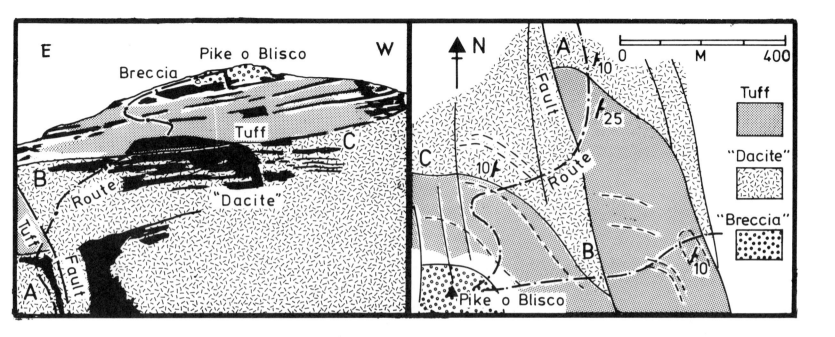

Figure 30 Sketch and map relating to figure 29

PIKE O'BLISCO FROM MICKLEDEN
(NY 274 063)

Most mountains appear quite different from different viewpoints, and this applies to the geology as well as to the scenery. It is often the case, for example, that a geological structure shows up well only from one particular location. This is why High Snockrigg was especially selected for the view of the High Stile range (figure 11); similarly the structure of the Band (figure 35) can be seen only from certain positions, and Bowfell, Great Gable, Scafell and many other Lake District mountains are comparable in this respect. The view of Pike o'Blisco from Mickleden (figure 29) is only 1 kilometre west of that from the Old Dungeon Ghyll Hotel (figure 27) and whilst it is clearly the same mountain with the same geological structure, there are differences in perspective. For example, figure 29 shows a sudden break in the crags in the middle of the field of view, and another break just to the left of the summit which appears different from that in figure 27. It is likely that these structures represent major joints rather than faults, since there appears to be no displacement of strata along them. Other parts of Pike o'Blisco are by no means as straightforward as this. If the mountain is approached from the east via Bleaberry Knott, the rock succession below the tuffs is quite different from that shown here in that it consists of alternations of ignimbrite and dacite, (Moseley, 1983a), whilst the south-western slopes consist mostly of andesite lava rather than dacite. There are many volcanological problems still to be solved in this area and I await with interest the results of University and Geological Survey research now in progress.

Figure 31   A coarse and bedded tuff sequency, Pike o'Blisco

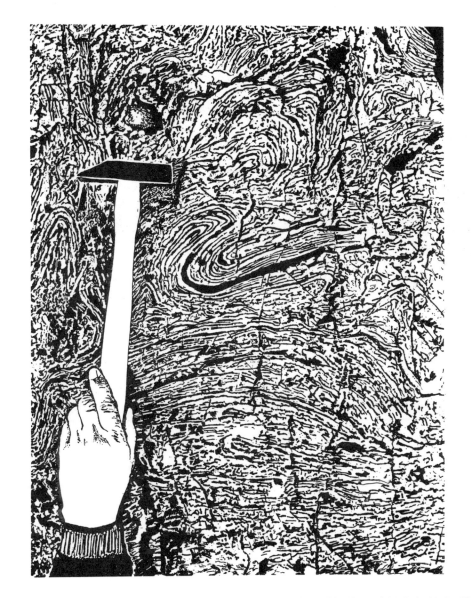

Figure 32 Slump folds in bedded tuff

Slump folding of bedding

BORROWDALE
VOLCANIC TUFF

During vulcanicity the
unconsolidated ash slumped
down gentle slopes to form
these small scale folds.
The deposit formed under
water.

Figure 33   Outcrop of bedded tuff, Pike o'Blisco

BEDDED TUFF, PIKE O'BLISCO

The bedded tuffs of Pike o'Blisco resemble those described on Honister and were formed in the same way. Most of them are volcaniclastic sediments, the ashfall eventually ending up in water, probably rivers and shallow lakes, where it was redistributed by currents. Certain parts of the sequence, however, are more likely to have been formed by ash falling directly on to land (figure 31). In the lower part of that section a coarse tuff or breccia contains flattened fragments, suggesting there may have been some ignimbrite mechanism involved in the eruption (see figure 37). Hence it may have been formed sub-aerially. Overlying this bed with an irregular contact is bedded tuff displaying sedimentary structures which suggest deposition in water, possibly in a river. The highest layer is unbedded medium to coarse tuff, and was probably airfall on land.

Figure 33 is typical of many of the low outcrops of bedded tuff found on the slopes of Pike o'Blisco. It is a rock of spectacular appearance and is easy to identify. Close to, current ripples, cross-lamination and slumping, including small contemporaneous faults, can be seen. Figure 34 shows small faults of this type.

— CLAY—SILT GRADE

— VARIABLE
  MOSTLY COARSE GRAIN

— CLAY GRADE

— MEDIUM — COARSE SAND GRADE

— CLAY GRADE

— MEDIUM—COARSE SAND GRADE

— ALTERNATING SILT—FINE SAND—SAND
  (NOTE THE (SLUMP) FAULTS AT **X**)

Figure 34 A detail of bedded tuff, Pike o'Blisco

Figure 35   Crinkle Crags and the Band from White Crag

The Band to Bowfell
(1:25 000 map NY20)

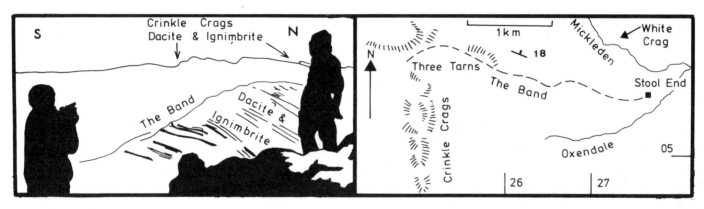

Figure 36 Map and sketch illustrating figure 35

The pathway up the Band is the route followed by most of those ascending Crinkle Crags and Bowfell. It leads to the col at Three Tarns (figure 36) and then branches, with Crinkle Crags to the left and Bowfell to the right. Many years ago I recall walking along this path to Bowfell and being completely mystified by the geology of the Band, even though there are numerous outcrops. This is a problem which is resolved by distant views such as those of figures 24 and 35, in which the different layers of rock can be seen to dip steadily from left to right with each layer corresponding to a different bed of lava or ignimbrite (see also figures 36 and 40). To examine the geology, the ascent of the Band should be accomplished in easy stages, otherwise interesting outcrops will be missed; it also provides a good excuse for more elderly geologists to pause for breath. The path starts at Stool End (NY 277 057), and here one can become acquainted with faintly pink, flinty-looking dacite lava. Higher up there are excellent exposures of eutaxitic ignimbrite (figures 37 and 38). British Geological Survey and University research workers are currently examining details of this succession. From Three Tarns the route across Crinkle Crags was described in a field itinerary by Moseley (1983a), and that across Bowfell is referred to below (figure 41).

IGNIMBRITE

Ignimbrite is associated with the most violent of all volcanic explosions. It is usually silica-rich and derived from a viscous magma under high gas pressure, the eruption perhaps triggered by some outside event such as an earthquake. The erupted material is incandescent, and its molten constituents are compressed into lenticular fragments by the weight of overlying material. The fragments solidify as black glass and appear on rock outcrops as black streaks (fiamme) set in a fine-grained, rather flinty, pale matrix. The texture is referred to as eutaxitic, and the glass has long since devitrified to a quartz–feldspar–chlorite mosaic.

The appearance of an ignimbrite hand specimen from the Band is shown on figure 37. Figure 38 is an enlargement showing that the streaky texture runs through the matrix. There is also a feldspar component of crystals already solid at the time of eruption.

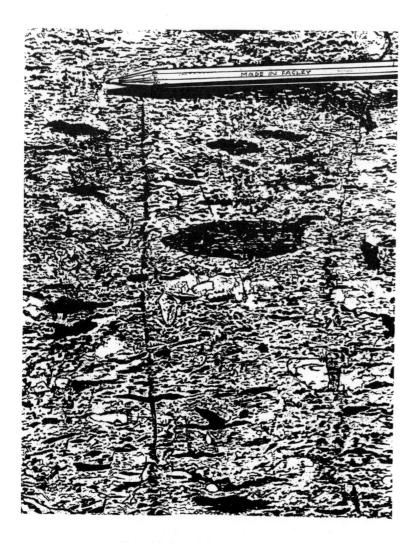

Figure 37 Ignimbrite outcrop on the Band

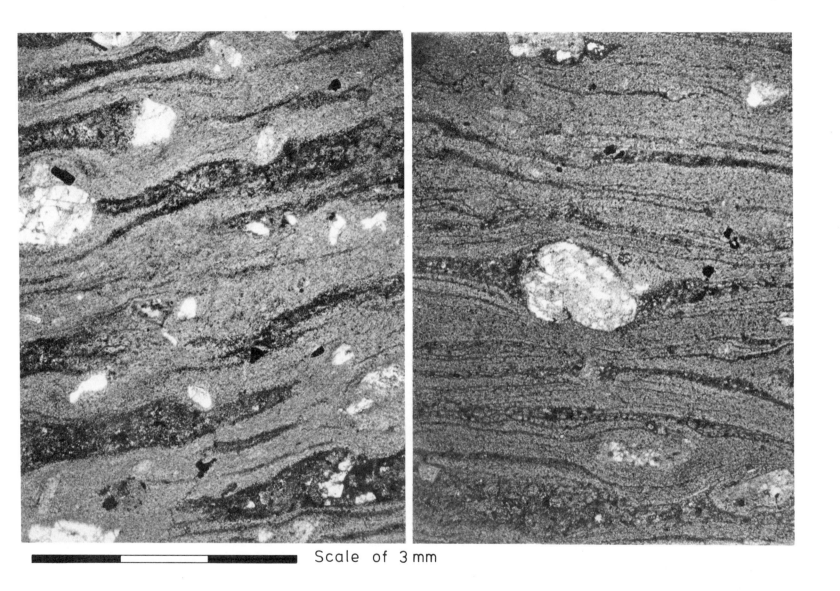

Scale of 3 mm

Figure 38   Enlargements of two ignimbrites; notice the eutaxitic (streaky) texture

Figure 39   Bowfell from Mickleden

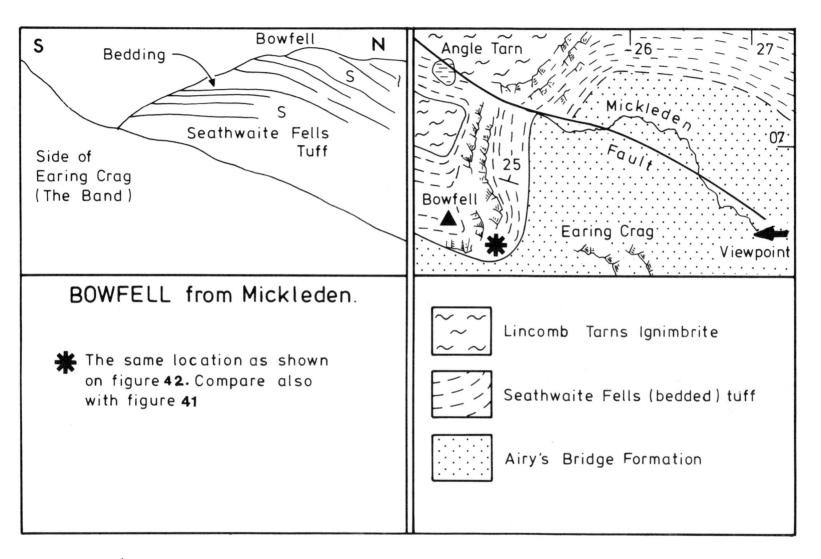

S | Bedding | Bowfell | **N**

S

S

Seathwaite Fells Tuff

Side of
Earing Crag
(The Band)

Angle Tarn

−26− 27

Mickleden

Fault

25

07

Bowfell ▲

Earing Crag

Viewpoint

BOWFELL from Mickleden.

✴ The same location as shown
on figure **42**. Compare also
with figure **41**

~~~ Lincomb Tarns Ignimbrite

⫽ Seathwaite Fells (bedded) tuff

⋯ Airy's Bridge Formation

Figure 40 Explanatory map and section for figure 39

Figure 41 Bowfell and the Churns of Bowfell from the south

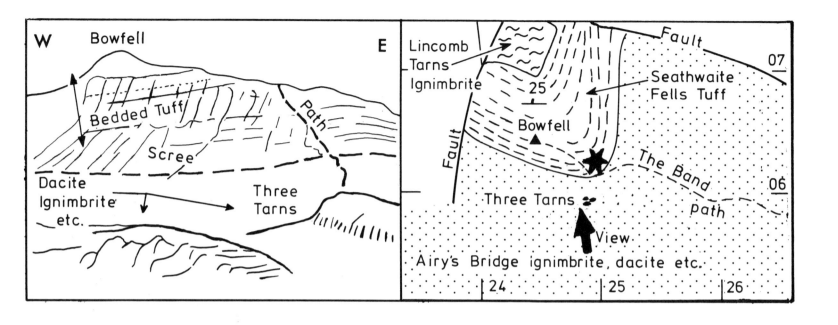

Figure 42 Map and sketch to explain figure 41

BOWFELL

A wide scree-like footpath rises from Three Tarns to the top of Bowfell, unnecessarily wide because of erosion by thousands of tramping feet, not all following exactly the same route. The route crosses from the Airy's Bridge Formation on to the Seathwaite Fells Tuffs just above the Three Tarns col (figures 41 and 42). The same geological horizon is shown on figure 22, and crosses the upper parts of the Langdale Pikes (Moseley, 1983a). From a distance the geology of Bowfell is easy to see, the Churns of Bowfell in particular showing the strong banding which results from alternating coarser and finer grained tuff.

The Seathwaite Fells Tuff is widespread in this part of the Lake District, and formed during one episode in the history of the Borrowdale Volcano. It is worth repeating that similar eruptive events occurred both before and after the Seathwaite Fells Tuff was deposited. Examples include the Honister Tuffs, already described, and the Tilberthwaite Tuffs of Coniston. The eruptive processes producing such tuffs eventually resulted in deposition of volcanic ash in water, with all the great variety of sedimentary structures associated with these conditions (see figures 33 and 34, and also figure 43).

Figure 43 Difficult rocks from the Borrowdale Volcanics. (A) Flow-banded 'dacite' lava. The bands were formed by flow in a viscous liquid. These rocks are easily mistaken for bedded tuff (see figures 33 and 34), but can be distinguished by careful inspection with a hand lens. Dacite and rhyolite lava have an igneous texture, usually with small rectangular phenocrysts (figure 20) set in a 'flinty', one time glassy, matrix whereas the tuff is composed of angular fragments of varying size. (B) Flow-brecciated andesite lava. These lavas are viscous and during flow the cooling crust often becomes semi-solid and is broken into fragments by pressure from the still molten interior of the flow. Ancient lavas of this kind often resemble other volcanic rocks made up of angular fragments, such as agglomerate formed by explosion, and mudflow (see Moseley, 1983, page 14)

Figure 44   Helm Crag, Grasmere

Helm Crag, Grasmere (1:25 000 map NY30)

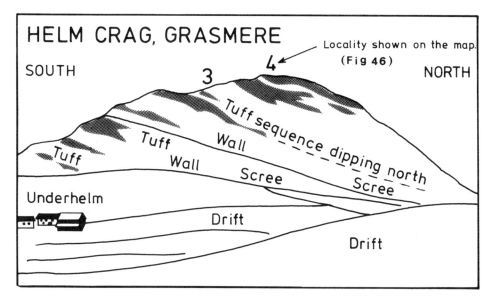

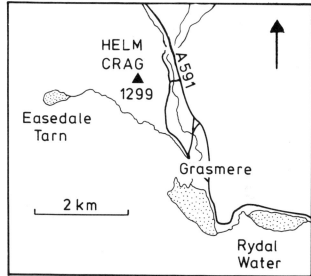

Figure 45   Explanatory sketch and location map for Helm Crag

Wordsworth ensured that Grasmere would remain one of the most popular centres in the Lake District, and of the many walks in this region, I imagine that the ascent of Helm Crag with its beautiful views all the way to the summit, is one of the best known. It is not an arduous walk; I have seen many a three-year-old cantering along the summit ridge, and it is easily accessible from Grasmere village. A convenient car park is indicated on figure 46 (NY 334 080), beyond which it is not easy to park vehicles without inconvenience to local residents. From locality 1 (NY 327 086, figure 46) a new path has been constructed, replacing an old path which was becoming badly eroded. Walkers should keep to this new route, not only to prevent further erosion, but also because it crosses the best geology. The geology of the region is in fact quite straightforward, with layers of tuff, resulting from volcanic explosions, dipping at about 20° to 30° to the north. The dip is a result of the Caledonian Earth Movements which tilted the rocks to these angles, and it does not, for example, represent deposition on the slopes of a former volcano; the rocks were originally deposited in near-horizontal layers. The distant view (figure 44) shows the dip of the strata, each escarpment being composed of relatively harder and generally coarser-grained tuff, with the scree-covered benches between the escarpments made up of more easily eroded 'bedded' tuffs (alternations of medium and fine grained fragments). The escarpments can be seen to descend the hillside towards the north, and the rock layers forming them can be examined during a walk to the summit.

Locality 1 (figure 46, NY 327 086). In this area there are several abandoned quarries where poorly bedded medium to coarse tuff was formerly worked for slate. The absence of distinct bedding planes indicates that, at the time, the volcano was raining down a continuous supply of debris, and the tuffs are likely to have accumulated quickly. The quarrying was made easier by the near-vertical cleavage, imposed by the stresses of the Caledonian mountain building when the mica, chlorite and clay minerals (phyllosilicates) recrystallised to become aligned at right angles to the stresses. The rock now splits in this direction (figure 7).

Locality 2 (NY 327 087). Hereabouts the footpath slants gently up the hillside and crosses outcrops of bedded tuff. The alternations of coarser and finer material, and the inclination of the layers, are clearly seen alongside the footpath. This type of bedded tuff was deposited some distance from the erupting vent on the flank of the volcano. Comparison with modern volcanoes suggests that the tuffs were laid down during a period when alternating strong and weak explosive eruptions threw out coarser and finer material, with considerable time intervals between eruptions.

Locality 3 (NY 328 091). The footpath bends sharply to the right and at a good viewpoint joins the old path and bends to the left again. Grasmere and the fells to the south are well seen from here, but it is not easy to pick out the distant geology. Bedded tuffs similar to those of locality 2 cross the footpath, dipping about 30° to the north.

Localities 4 and 5 (NY 326 093). The opposite ends of the summit ridge are dominated by the sentinels of the 'lion' and the 'lamb', two up-standing rock buttresses visible from the main road below. To my knowledge they have no especial geological significance, and the whole of the summit ridge is made up of coarser and finer tuffs. Those near to the 'lion' admittedly have some unusual characteristics which would repay further investigation.

Locality 6 (NY 327 093). Immediately to the east of the summit ridge there is a rather chaotic hummocky area mostly composed of coarse tuffs, and a few yards further east, a low linear ridge trends northwards. It is made up of a dark fine-grained rock which I identify as basalt, and interpret as a dyke associated with local volcanicity.

Once on the top of Helm Crag it is well worth while pottering around, examining all the outcrops, and taking in distant views. The fells to the north especially reveal structures which one may be tempted to explore.

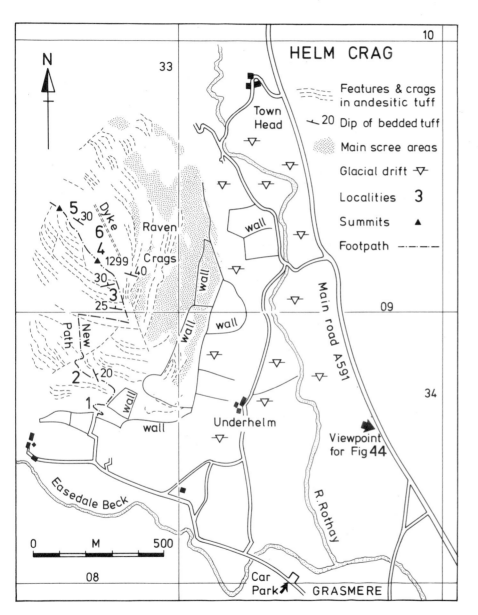

Figure 46 Detailed geological map of Helm Crag

HELM CRAG

Features & crags in andesitic tuff

⌐20 Dip of bedded tuff

Main scree areas

Glacial drift ▽

Localities 3

Summits ▲

Footpath —·—·—

Town Head

Raven Crags

▲ 1299

New Path

Underhelm

Viewpoint for Fig 44

Main road A591

R. Rothay

Easedale Beck

0   M   500

Car Park GRASMERE

10

33

09

34

08

Figure 47   Dove Crag from the east

Dove Crag
(1:25 000 map NY31)

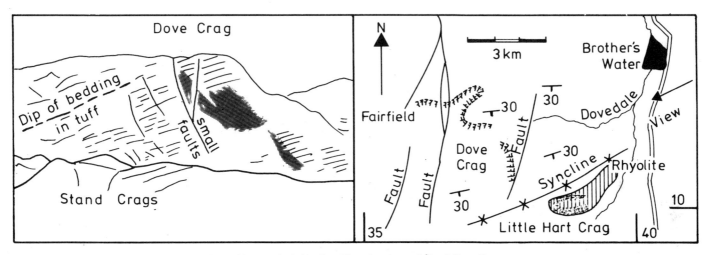

Figure 48 Map and sketch to illustrate the geology of Dove Crag

The view of Dove Crag shown in figure 47 can be seen from near Brother's Water, especially if binoculars are used. It is often the case in the Lake District that geological structure is not immediately apparent in the distant views of fellsides and has to be cultivated and reconsidered after careful inspection. Dove Crag is made of tuff, formerly volcanic ash, thrown out by the explosive activity of the Borrowdale Volcano and subsequently tilted by earth movements, so that it now dips at about 30° to the south. Close inspection of the crag reveals that much of the tuff is bedded (figures 33 and 34). Small faults (fractures which were formerly earthquake zones) have been eroded into gullies which are clearly visible (figure 48). Most are well known to rock climbers.

The view of figure 47 is a view for motorists, who may pause during the ascent or descent of Kirkstone Pass. I suggest that they inspect Dove Crag carefully and attempt to see the structures that I have indicated.

Figure 49   Fairfield from St. Sunday Crag

56

10

Fairfield
(1:25 000 map NY31)

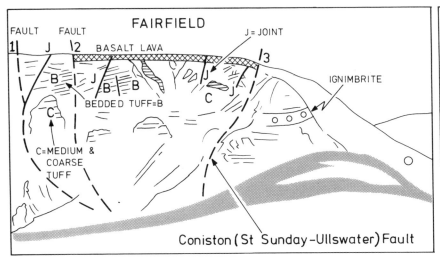

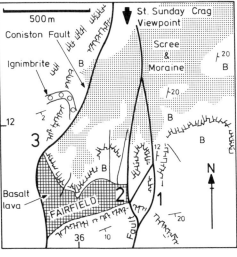

Figure 50 Map and sketch to illustrate the geology of Fairfield

There are many ways to climb Fairfield and many thousands do so each year. It can be approached from Patterdale and St. Sunday Crag, from Brother's Water and Deepdale, from Dovedale, from Kirkstone Pass or from the Grasmere side of the ridge — all equally attractive routes. At 860 metres it is one of the higher Lake District summits and in summer it can be benign; I have seen many family parties ambling across the flat summit area. However, beware! Even in summer, conditions can change rapidly and the bright sunshine of one hour can become the cold wind and rain-laden clouds of the next. Mist is the deceiver; a compass and adequate clothing in a rucksack break the spell, and will also save Mountain Rescue teams a lot of bother. In winter, conditions can be Alpine with cornices overlapping the north-facing precipices, and suitable gear for these conditions is necessary.

Most of the area between Kirkstone Pass and Helvellyn is made up of airfall tuffs of the

Borrowdale Volcanic Group, although there are subsidiary acid and basic lavas and ignimbrites (Moseley, 1972). Fairfield itself is capped by basalt lava which is underlain by a thick sequence of airfall andesitic tuffs. These are mostly bedded in alternations of coarser and finer fragments, the layering being clearly seen in distant views (see also figures 31 to 34).

The whole of this area is traversed by a number of faults, some of which are shown on figure 50. The displacement of strata across most of them is difficult to determine but, with one exception, is probably small. The exception is the Coniston to Ullswater Fault which is one of the largest in the Lake District. Near Coniston, where it is easier to measure, there is a horizontal displacement of the Coniston Limestone of over 1 kilometre (figure 51).

11

Tarn Hows and the Coniston Limestone
(1:25 000 maps NY30 and SD39)

The small lake of Tarn Hows with its surroundings is undoubtedly one of the best known beauty spots in the Lake District. It is compact, beautifully wooded, supplied with concealed car parks and well provided with footpaths, some of which cater for wheel-chairs. It is a place for a delightful family stroll, one which includes toddlers and grandparents. It is also a place of great geological interest. The junction between the Borrowdale Volcanics and the Coniston Limestone crosses the area, and there is a great deal of structural interest, mostly in the nature of the faulting. The geology can be treated at elementary and advanced levels. The former should be comprehensible to all with a geological interest, but full understanding will evade all but the expert (McNamara, 1979).

The oldest rocks of Tarn Hows, the Borrowdale Volcanics, are nearly all airfall tuffs composed of small angular fragments of volcanic rocks, but they are not easy to identify (locality 8, figure 51). The rocks of the Coniston Limestone Formation rest unconformably upon them; that is, there was a time gap of many millions of years between the deposition of the two sequences, during which vast quantities of volcanic materials were removed by erosion. The Coniston Limestone Formation is not a true limestone but is the name given to a sequence of rocks which includes sandstones, limestones, mudstones and shales. The lowest rocks in the sequence are in fact sandstones and conglomerates (the Long Sleddale Member) which were formed by erosion of the underlying volcanic rocks, followed by redeposition in shallow marine embayments. The episode has been dated by the contained shelly fossils. The principal limestones rest on these sandstones. There is relatively pure limestone at the base although exposure is patchy, but higher up the sequence the limestone becomes increasingly nodular, forming rounded lumps separated by dark mudstone (locality 3, figure 51, and figure 53). Still higher, the limestones disappear and the sequence becomes entirely mudstone (Torver and Troutbeck Members), and eventually in the depression just beyond the top of the low crags (figure 52) the Ashgill Shale outcrops. The 3 metre thick White Limestone (figure 51) is badly exposed, and I have only seen it in the woods (SD 323 988, locality 2).

Above the Coniston Limestone Formation the sequence continues with the Skelgill Shales and Browgill Shales of lower Silurian age (Ingham *et al.*, 1978). The former are black shales which were laid down in deep sea and are rich in graptolites, small animals which dropped to the sea floor on death and accumulated in the muds. These rocks are soft, easily eroded and therefore badly exposed, but may be inspected along the stream course at locality 2. The Browgill Shales are grey mudstones which grade upwards into the striped mudstones of the Brathay Flags, described under figures 55 to 58.

The Brathay Flags are transitional upwards into the greywacke sandstone–mudstone alternations of the Coldwell Formation. These beds can be inspected at locality 1 (High Cross Quarry). This quarry is important because of the orthocones preserved on some bedding surfaces These are rather obscure cone-shaped

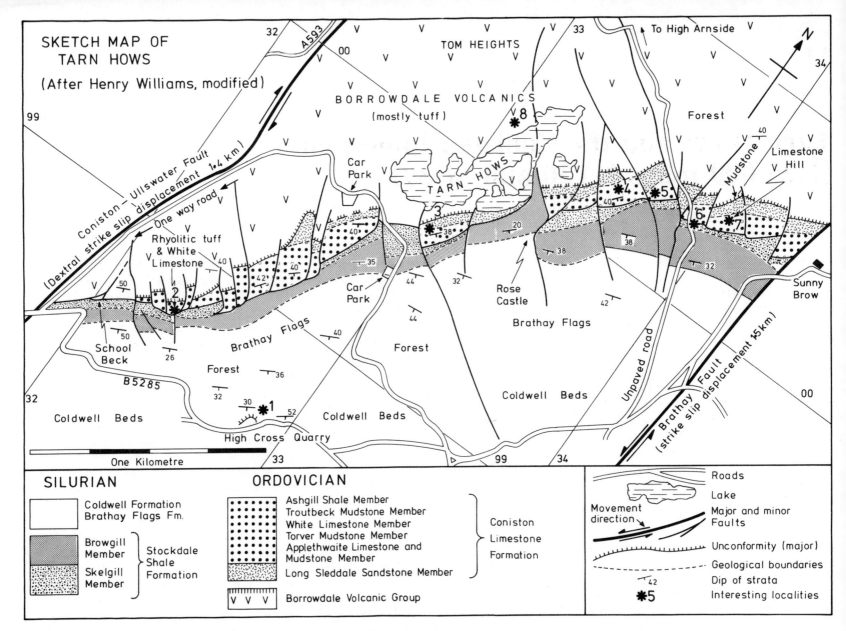

Figure 51 Geological map of Tarn Hows

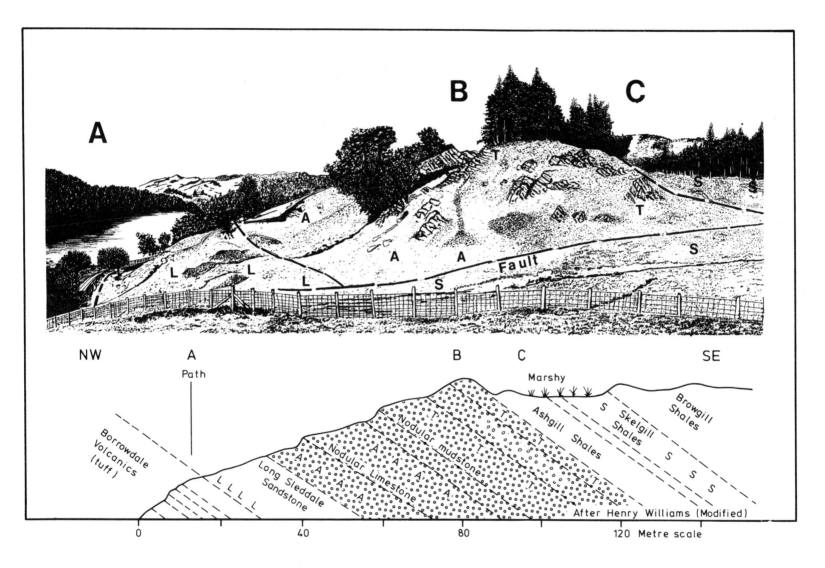

Figure 52 View of locality 3, Tarn Hows, showing the Coniston Limestone sequence referred to on figure 51. L – Long Sleddale, A – Applethwaite, T – Torver to Troutbeck, S – Skelgill

61

Figure 53 Part of the view from locality 3, Tarn Hows. See figure 52. The section is from higher beds of the Coniston Limestone Formation and is predominantly in cleaved mudstone, although there are numerous calcareous (limestone) concretions (see figure 54) which have been weathered out into holes (N)

fossils related to modern-day cuttle fish, and visitors are requested not to damage them. In this quarry the dip steepens from less than 30° to more than 50°.

The structures of this area are just as inter-esting and important as the geological succession. The rocks were tilted at 30° to 50° to the south-east by the Caledonian earth movements at the end of the Silurian. They were also cleaved with cleavage planes dipping at about 70° to the north-west (see also figures 55 and 64). More interesting are the faults, former Caledonian earthquake zones along which the rocks are displaced. Tarn Hows is sandwiched between two of the largest faults in the Lake District (figure 51). Both are wrench faults, that is the displacement is largely horizontal and in each case it approximates to $1\frac{1}{2}$ kilo-metres. In the west, the one-way road from Tarn Hows to Coniston (SD 320 990) slants down the escarpment made by the Coniston-Ullswater Fault. This is a result of differential erosion between the soft Brathay Flags to the west and the hard volcanics to the east. The Brathay Flags form the lower ground as far as the main Coniston-Ambleside road. This fault has a dextral movement, that is if one faces the fault the far side has moved to the right. From a theoretical standpoint it is unusual for a north–south fault to have dextral movment in the Lake District. The Coniston Fault can be traced northwards to Grasmere, where it splits into two, one branch traversing Dunmail Raise and Thirlmere to end in the Vale of St. John, and the other ending in the Skiddaw Slate out-crop of Ullswater (Soper and Moseley, 1978, figure 23). Southwards it runs into Coniston Water, rotates locally into a thrust, and even-tually joins up with the Beacon Tarn fault system (figure 59). The Brathay Fault displaces the rocks in the opposite (sinisträl) sense to the Coniston Fault. It forms an escarpment in the Sunny Brow region and, to the north, ends near Ullswater. Of the smaller faults, some parallel the dip but others are at right angles to the dip (parallel to the strike) so that whole parts of the sequence are cut out. Note, for

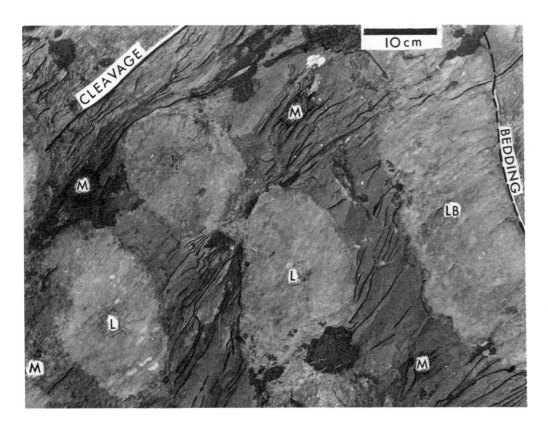

Figure 54 Applethwaite beds, locality 4, Tarn Hows. This is the typical Coniston Limestone with nodules (L) and beds (LB) of limestone alternating with dark mudstone (M). Notice the irregularity of bedding and the way the cleavage in softer mudstone bends round the harder nodules of limestone

example, that adjacent to locality 3 Skelgill Shales rest against Borrowdale Volcanics, and the whole of the Coniston Limestone is missing.

I have not mentioned localities 4 to 7 which are in the east of the Tarn Hows area, and are accessible from the unpaved road which leads to High Arnside. The whole of the Coniston Limestone sequence can be inspected near Limestone Hill, both east and west of the road (localities 4, 5 and 7) and the Skelgill Shales are exposed at the roadside (locality 6).

It is easy to walk from Tarn Hows to this area, but it means climbing a fence and is therefore not recommended. Tarn Hows is carefully maintained by the National Trust, and fences are expensive items constructed from meagre resources. They are easily damaged and broken down and therefore should not be climbed.

Figure 55   Banishead Quarry and the Torver Beck waterfall

12

The Brathay Flags of Banishead, Coniston (1:25 000 map SD29)

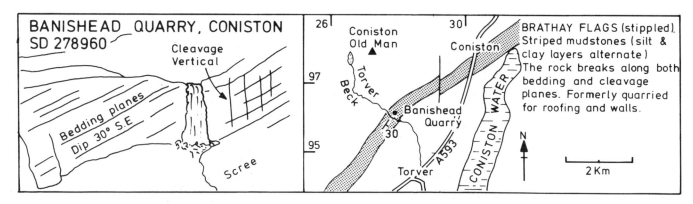

BANISHEAD QUARRY, CONISTON
SD 278960
Cleavage Vertical
Bedding planes Dip 30° S.E
Scree

26 | Coniston Old Man | 30 |
97
Torver Beck
Coniston
Banishead Quarry
30
95
Torver
A4593
CONISTON WATER
N
2 Km

BRATHAY FLAGS (stippled). Striped mudstones (silt & clay layers alternate) The rock breaks along both bedding and cleavage planes. Formerly quarried for roofing and walls.

Figure 56 Explanatory sketch and map for Banishead Quarry

The Brathay Flags Formation, which is approximately 200 metres thick, forms a narrow outcrop across the whole of the Lake District (Ingham *et al.*, 1978). The dip is usually to the south-east at 30° to 40°, although there are a few minor folds in some areas, Tarn Hows for example. The lithology is unique in the Lake District, consisting of uniform, fine-scale alternations of paler silt and darker mud as shown on figure 58. It will be noticed that there are approximately 10 layers per centimetre. The

indications are that these striped mudstones accumulated quietly and steadily in a clay-rich sea.

The rocks were tilted to their present attitude and cleaved by the Caledonian mountain building movements at the end of the Silurian Period (figures 53, 54 and 57). Both bedding and cleavage show up well in Banishead Quarry.

The Brathay Flags are soft, easily eroded rocks and form low-lying ground with few natural exposures. There are, however, quite a few old quarries where details can be investi-

gated, and of these Banishead Quarry is the most attractive and has open access. The Torver Beck waterfall which plunges into it is one of the most impressive in the Lake District, especially when the stream is in spate. Good footpaths lead past Banishead Quarry. It may be approached from Little Arrow, near Torver (SD 290 950) and from Coniston via the steep road towards Coniston Old Man (cars can be left at the fell gate) (SD 289 971). Details of this area are given in Moseley, 1983a, excursion Ga.

Figure 57 Enlargement of Banishead Quarry and the Torver Beck waterfall

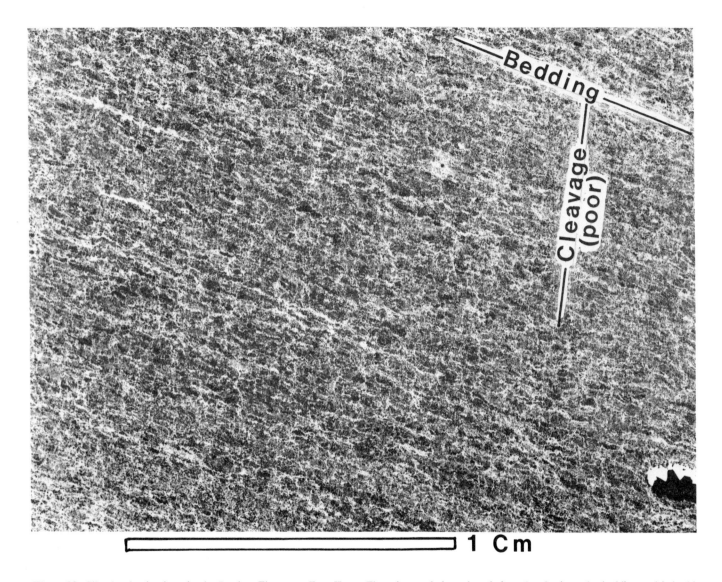

Figure 58   Silt–clay laminations in the Brathay Flags near Tarn Hows. The micas and clay minerals form bands along the bedding and it is this which gives the striped appearance to the Brathay Flags

Figure 59 Map showing the location and general geology of the Beacon Tarn area

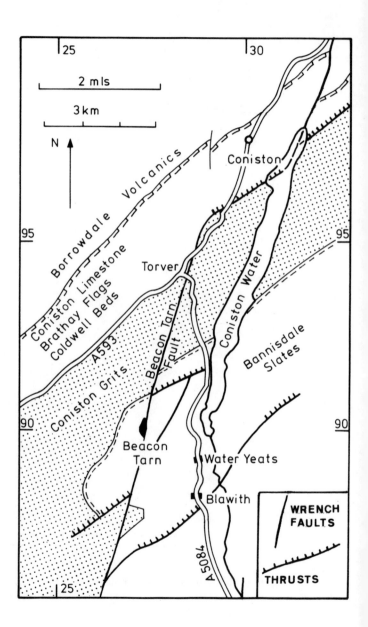

13

The Bannisdale Slates of Blawith Common and Beacon Tarn (1:25 000 maps SD28 and SD29)

Here we have a beautiful area, surprisingly far from the madding crowd and well off the beaten track, even though it is so close to Coniston Water. It is undulating ground rising to 260 m above OD on the Beacon and has numerous small rocky knobs sticking up through the bracken and heather. Most of the rocks fall within the Bannisdale Slate Formation of Silurian age. They are banded mudstones with occasional massive greywacke sandstone ribs, which are more resistant to erosion and form ridges as indicated on figure 60. The banding in the mudstones is caused by the numerous paler silty laminae.

It is, however, the structure which provides the greatest interest. The rocks were strongly folded, cleaved and faulted during the Caledonian earth movements and all these structures are easy to see on the ground (Moseley, 1983b).

Folding. Inspection of figure 60 will show that in the west between Beacon Tarn and the Beacon the rocks dip steadily to the south-east, folding becoming prominent farther south-east towards the road. The effects of weathering have resulted in harder bands standing out as ribs, or being exposed as bedding planes which can be followed across fold axes with no difficulty. The axes plunge (incline) to the south-east at angles of 25° to 30° as shown on figure 61.

Cleavage. The mudstones in particular were partially recrystallised by the Caledonian stresses, and as slates they now split along these cleavage planes as well as along the bedding. It will be noticed that the cleavage is very nearly parallel to the axial planes of the folds, whilst the relation between bedding, cleavage and fold plunge is shown on figure 61.

Faults. There are three interesting faults within the area of figure 60. The most obvious is the Beacon Tarn Fault which has eroded out to provide the site for Beacon Tarn, and extends northwards as a low marshy gully. It is a sinistral* wrench fault with a horizontal displacement of about half a mile and is one of the most important faults in the southern Lake District (Soper and Moseley, 1978). Another important wrench fault east of the Beacon trends NNE and has also eroded out to form a marshy depression. The third fault, the Beacon Fault is perhaps the most interesting. In the south it is aligned north-west–south-east, but swings round the Beacon to follow a north-east trend. It is best interpreted as a thrust. It may be noted that in the southern Lake District, T. N. Norman mapped a number of composite wrench–thrust faults (Soper and Moseley, 1978, figure 28, and this book figure 59).

Microgranite. The route from localities 1 to 6 crosses several outcrops of pink Caledonian microgranite. They are no more than scrappy exposures at the edge of the footpath, apart from locality 6 which is well worth a visit. A

---

*'Sinistral' refers to the sense of movement. Stand facing the fault and the far side has moved to the left.

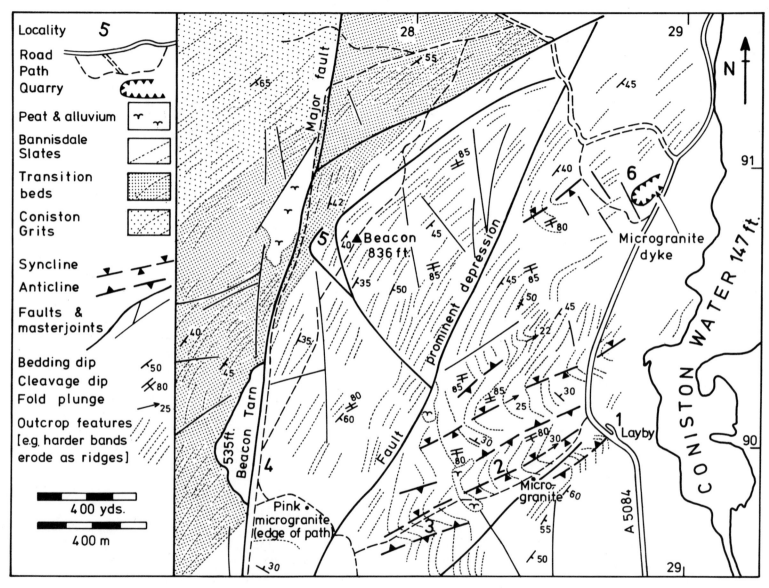

Figure 60 Geological map of Beacon Tarn and Blawith Common

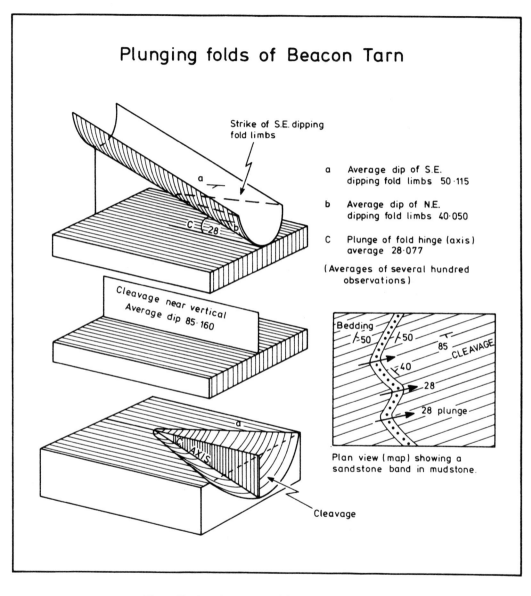

Plunging folds of Beacon Tarn

Strike of S.E. dipping fold limbs

a Average dip of S.E. dipping fold limbs 50·115

b Average dip of N.E. dipping fold limbs 40·050

C Plunge of fold hinge (axis) average 28·077

(Averages of several hundred observations)

Cleavage near vertical
Average dip 85·160

Bedding

Bedding ⌐50   ⌐50   ⊤85 CLEAVAGE

40

28

28 plunge

Plan view (map) showing a sandstone band in mudstone.

AXIS

Cleavage

Figure 61 Drawing to explain the structures of Beacon Tarn

wide vertical microgranite dyke has been quarried, leaving only a thin layer of microgranite attached to each wall of the quarry, so that the intrusive contacts with the Bannisdale Slates can be studied. The whole width of the dyke can be seen in the back wall of the quarry.

Excursion route. The most convenient excursion route (figure 60) follows a series of footpaths. It will be found that progress away from the paths is hampered in summer by high banks of bracken.

Locality 1. There is ample parking at this point. A sharp anticline will be seen in a 4 metre high outcrop on the west side of the road, and there are other folds on the east side of the road a few metres to the north.

Locality 2. Follow the footpath towards locality 1. A plunging syncline outlined by bedding planes in a harder rock band is prominent to the north.

Locality 3. A synclinal fold axis coincides with the path. Detours to north and south will reveal other folds.

Locality 4. The straight line eastern margin of Beacon Tarn marks the line of the fault. There are now two alternative routes: either take the path across the Beacon or that which follows the line of the fault.

Locality 5. The former route will allow one to investigate the evidence for the Beacon Thrust referred to above.

Locality 6. Footpaths can be followed leading to the microgranite quarry already described.

14

The Coniston Grits and Bannisdale Slates of Shap (1:25 000 maps NY50 and NY60)

Well known localities in the Shap area are the granite and andesite quarries, the metamorphic aureole and the Carboniferous–Silurian unconformity at Shap Wells. The area south of Shap Summit described here is perhaps not so well known but it is interesting. The exposed rocks are Coniston Grits and Bannisdale Slates of Silurian age, outcropping in the major Bannisdale Syncline which crosses the greater part of the Lake District. It will be noticed that the syncline is displaced by two north-west trending dextral wrench faults* within the area of figure 62. In addition to the major syncline there are numerous minor folds (parasitic folds, that is they are part of the same fold phase), especially in the Bannisdale Slates. The rocks also have a moderate cleavage.

I will first give an outline itinerary starting at Shap Summit and finishing at Jeffrey's Mount (figure 66), and then go into a few more details. The chosen route starts at Crookdale Crag where the section beside the A6 shows the rocks to be

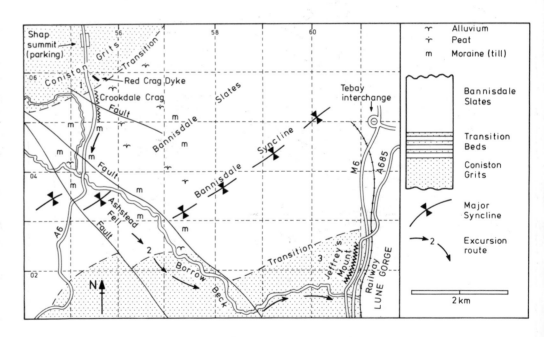

Figure 62 Geological map of the south Shap area

*Wrench faults have horizontal displacement and 'dextral' refers to the fact that if one stands facing the fault the far side has moved to the right.

strongly folded. The road is followed to Borrow Beck and then one strikes across Ashstead Fell, where numerous folds will be seen in the Bannisdale Slates, but they become less common in the stronger (competent) Coniston Grits. Continue to the A685 and folding of the Coniston Grits in Jeffrey's Mount can be examined. It is desirable to have transport waiting at Jeffrey's Mount since it is a long walk back to Shap Summit.

The Crookdale Crag-Ashstead Fell area is shown in more detail on figure 63. In the north there is a microgranite dyke and, just south of this, the excellent A6 section (Moseley, 1968). The rocks are assigned to the Bannisdale Slates, but there are numerous greywacke sandstone beds in the section, indicating a wide transition zone from the grits to the slates proper. The sedimentology of this section is well worth close study, includ-

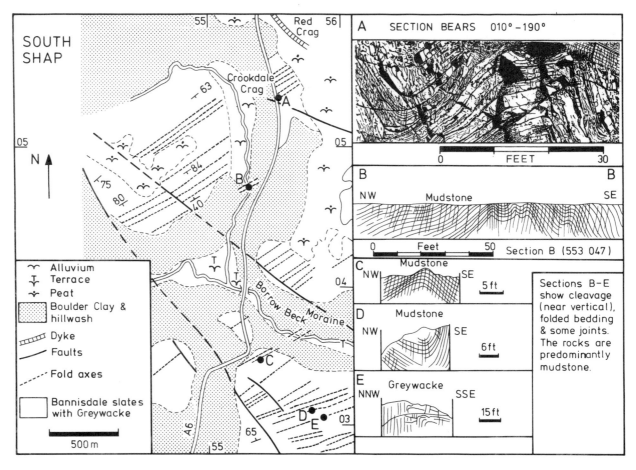

Figure 63   More detailed map and diagrams of south Shap

ing as it does almost all the turbidite lithologies. The presence of greywacke sandstone and siltstone beds, interbedded with the banded mudstones, makes for greater interest. There are eleven folds in the Crookdale Crag section, the two most southerly being illustrated at A (figure 63). All the folds are asymmetrical with steep, near-vertical, south-dipping limbs and more gentle (40° to 50°), north-dipping limbs. Cleavage is quite well developed and is slightly oblique to the axial planes of the folds. Figures 64

and 65 illustrate a detail of one of the vertical fold limbs. A 35 centimetre thick greywacke sandstone forms a graded bed and is followed by cleaved mudstone. It will be noticed that whereas no cleavage is developed in the greywacke, it is strong in the mudstone and about 20° oblique to the bedding. This is shown in more detail in the enlargement of the greywacke-mudstone junction, and is because the greywacke is a stronger rock composed mostly of quartz.

73

Figure 64   Vertical fold limb from the Crookdale Crag section showing a detail of a sandstone–mudstone junction

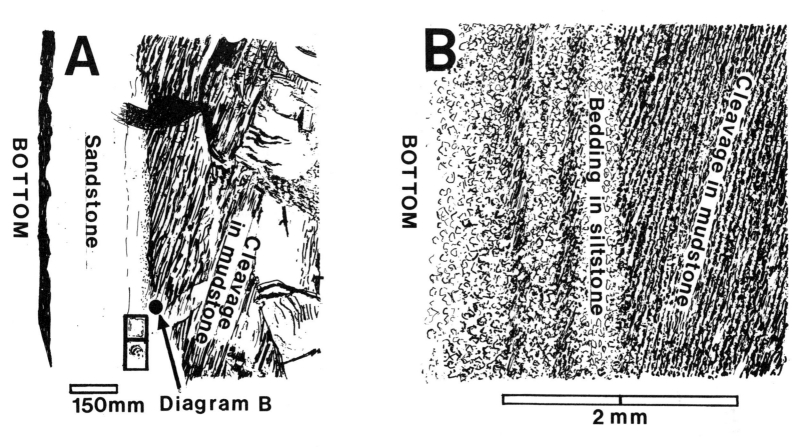

Figure 65 Explanatory diagrams of figure 62

Sections B to E are also within the Bannisdale Slates, but greywackes are now quite subsidiary. The folds at B and C are close to the axial region of the major syncline, and the folds are now symmetrical whereas those at D and E are on the north-dipping limb and are asymmetrical in the opposite sense of those of Crookdale Crag, with steep north-dipping limbs.

Some details of Jeffrey's Mount are shown on figures 66, 67 and 69 (Moseley, 1972). It provides an excellent section in the Coniston Grits, interesting both from sedimentological and structural points of view. There are eight folds in all, less tight than those in the slates because of the greater competence of these massive sandstones. Locally there are steeply dipping limbs and in a few cases the fold axis coincides with a fault. Details of two of the folds are shown in figures 67 and 68.

The road cut also shows some interesting engineering applications. The folds are almost at right angles to the road so that there is no slip-

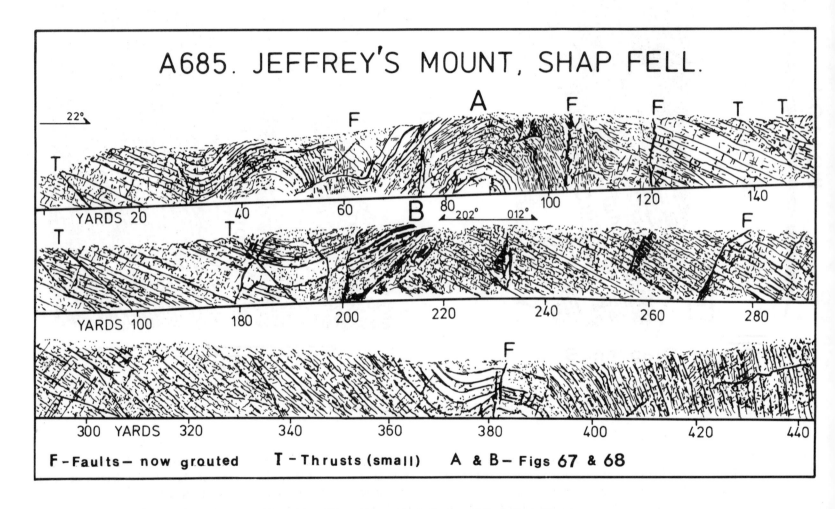

Figure 66   A685 roadside section in Coniston Grits, Jeffrey's Mount

page along bedding planes into the cutting. However, the small sinistral and dextral faults with parallel joints did pose some problems. The sinistral structures in particular make an oblique angle with the road, with the danger of slabs spalling off along joint planes to give rock falls. This problem was overcome by placing rock bolts to stabilise the joints.

The faults occur as shatter zones 0.5 metres wide, and carry quantities of water. It was necessary to grout them and pass the water in drains beneath the road.

There is an almost identical section alongside the M6 immediately below the A685, but this is inaccessible.

A – Fig 66

Figure 67 Anticline A, Jeffrey's Mount. See figure 66 for location

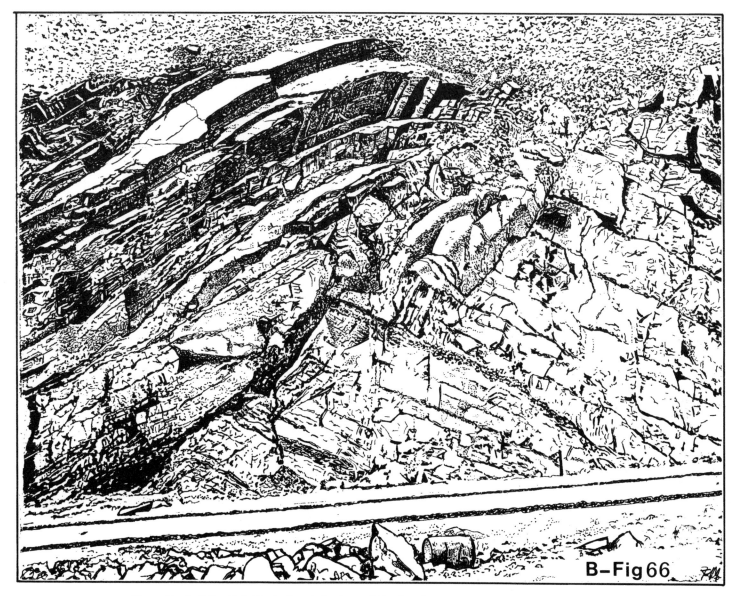

Figure 68   Anticline B, Jeffrey's Mount. See figure 66 for location

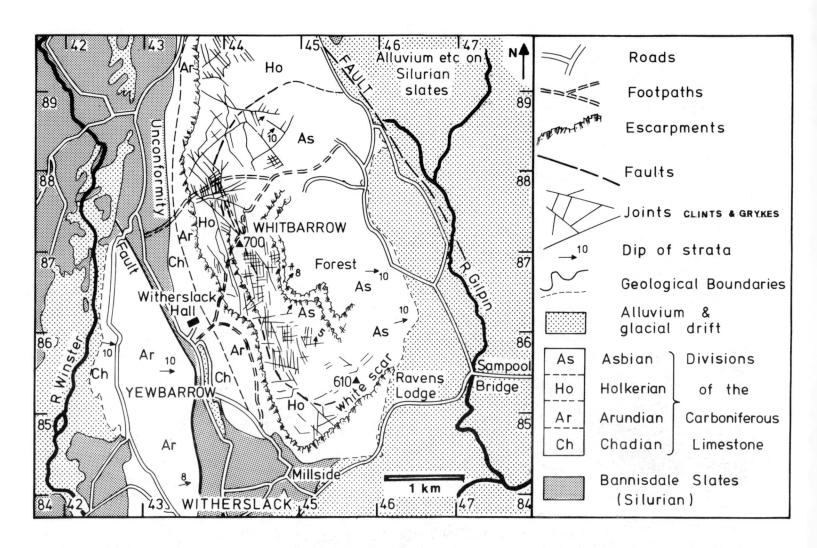

Figure 69 Geological map of the Whitbarrow area

15

Whitbarrow and the Carboniferous Limestone (1:25 000 map SD48)

Figure 70   Carboniferous Limestones of Whitbarrow Scar (White Scar) from the east

Take the new road from Levens to Barrow (incidentally, the quickest way to Coniston) and the first Lake District bastion to come into view is the striking Carboniferous Limestone escarpment of Whitbarrow (figure 70). The scenery of the Whitbarrow-Witherslack area is most attractive and well worth stopping to investigate. Indeed it compares in beauty with any part of the Lake District, but it is limestone scenery and therefore quite different in character from other areas. A delightful walk starts near Witherslack Hall, and follows the footpath through the woods and on to the limestone pavements of Whitbarrow summit (figures 69 and 70).

Most people with a general interest in geology do not need to subdivide the thick sequences of the Carboniferous Limestone, but specialists divide it up on the basis of fossils and lithologies. The fossil divisions are now given stage names (Arundian etc.), which are updated versions of the subdivisions made by Garwood in his classical papers of 1913 and 1916. The fossils relate to their environments, which also resulted in different lithologies. These include, at different horizons, oolitic limestone, dolomite, pseudobreccia, massive limestone and thinly bedded limtestone, all these features helping in correlation between one area and another. Once again the local variety of different limestone lithologies is for the specialist, and it requires careful inspection to determine that, for example, the rock is an oolite, and made up of small spherical grains. Dolomite closely resembles normal limestone in its field appearance but is composed of magnesium-calcium carbonate rather than calcium carbon-

Figure 71 Limestone pavement, Whitbarrow

ate, and pseudobreccia is an apparently fragmental rock but was formed by patchy crystallisation of a calcium carbonate mud.

For much of the time the Whitbarrow limestones were being laid down on the fringes of the Lake District, and an ancient Lower Palaeozoic landscape remained to the north. Full submergence did not occur until the Holkerian when limestone seas spread across most of the Lake District (Mitchell *et al.*, 1978). During Chadian times Whitbarrow was near a shoreline. There are some dolomites amongst the limestones and corals such as *Koninckophyllum, Thysanophyllum* and *Carcinophyllym* can be

found. The Arundian marine shelf produced different lithologies with some oolites and higher in the sequence some dolomite (the Gastropod Beds of Garwood). It contains such fossils as *Michelinia, Palaeosmilia, Caninia, Lithostrotion* and *Delepinea*. Fossils are not common in the Holkerian apart from crinoids, nor are they abundant in the Asbian. The latter is particularly noteworthy for the development of a karst topography with widespread clints and grykes (figure 71), although this type of topography can also occur at lower horizons.

The structure of the Whitbarrow limestone, at first sight simple, also has its interest.

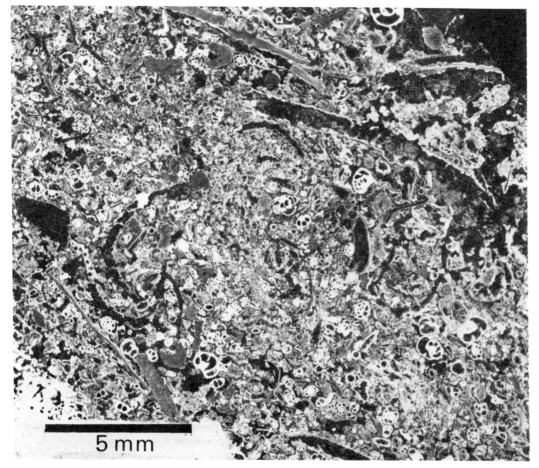

Figure 72 At first sight much of the Carboniferous Limestone may appear to be unfossiliferous. However, close inspection with a hand lens may reveal numerous microfossils and shell fragments in the matrix. In this example many foraminifera can be seen

5 mm

Whitbarrow and Yewbarrow are two fault blocks with the limestone dipping gently to the east and resting unconformably on the Bannisdale Slates. The slates were strongly folded during the Caledonian mountain building, and during the succeeding Devonian Period formed part of a tropical desert continent, rather like South Arabia of today. Some 50 million years later the Carboniferous seas encroached on to this continent.

In post-Carboniferous times, gentle earth movements resulted not only in tilting and faulting, but also gave close patterns of joints. The latter are now weathered out to give the clints and grykes of the limestone pavement (figures 69 and 71). Statistical analysis shows that their orientation is not random, but is related to the stresses operating at the time. There are three maxima with about 50 per cent trending NNW, 30 per cent north-west, and about 27 per cent east-west (Moseley and Ahmed, 1967).

A recommended excursion route following public footpaths is shown on figure 69, but it crosses a nature reserve, and parties are therefore asked not to stray too far from the path, remembering that geology is only one aspect of such an area. Further information can be obtain- from the Hervey Reserve, Ambleside.

The footpath starts near Witherslack Hall (SD 437 860) where there is limited parking, and ascends across sparsely fossiliferous limestone scars to Lord's Seat, just above 700 feet (SD 442 871). There are good views all round, and to the east are excellent examples of limestone pavement dipping about 10° east, with clints and grykes oriented along the master joint directions. Follow a cairned path for a few hundred yards to the north-west, and at SD 440 873 there is a good example of a glacial erratic resting on limestone. The erratic is a large block of Borrowdale Volcanic agglomerate, and was transported to its present position by ice. Further north (SD 439 873) a vein of haematite will be seen, following a northerly trending joint. It has, at one time, been worked in a small way and is an outlier of the former Furness iron ore field. Another path leads downhill to the road at SD 430 872.

16

Conclusion

I would like to conclude with the observation that in this book and the preceding one on *The Volcanic Rocks of the Lake District* I have listed geological excursions covering most of the region. However, the topography and geology are diverse and there are areas and subjects I have not dealt with. The geological literature on the Lake District is enormous, and even before 1973, when the Cumberland Geological Society published R. A. Smith's bibliography, there were more than 1000 books and papers, which included a number of field guides and reports of field excursions. Since then there have been many more, really too numerous to mention in the references given here.

Those who wish to obtain a list of what is available should consult Smith's bibliography, and back numbers of journals such as the *Proceedings of the Yorkshire Geological Society*, the *Proceedings of the Geologists Association* (including the field excursion guide by G. H. Mitchell), the *Mercian Geologist, Proceedings of the N.E. Lancs. Geologists Association*, the *Amateur Geologist*, the *Quaternary Research Association Handbook* (Cumberland field trip) and particularly the *Proceedings of the Cumberland Geological Society*. Field books include *Geological Excursions in Lakeland* by E. H. Shackleton and *The Lake District* by the Cumberland Geological Society.

References

Cumberland Geological Society (1982). *The Lake District*. Unwin, London

Faller, A. M. and Briden, J. C. (1978). Palaeomagnetism of Lake District rocks. In *The Geology of the Lake District*, ed. F. Moseley, Occasional Publication No. 3, Yorkshire Geological Society, Leeds, pp. 17-24

Firman, R. J. (1978). Intrusions. In *The Geology of the Lake District*, ed. F. Moseley, Occasional Publication No. 3, Yorkshire Geological Society, Leeds, pp. 146-63

Garwood, E. J. (1913). The Lower Carboniferous succession in the north-west of England. *Q. Jl. geol. Soc. Lond.*, **68**, 449-586

Garwood, E. J. (1916). The faunal succession in the Lower Carboniferous rocks of Westmorland and north Lancashire. *Proc. Geol. Ass.*, **27**, 1-43

Ingham, J. K., McNamara, K. J. and Rickards, R. B. (1978). The Upper Ordovician and Silurian rocks. In *The Geology of the Lake District*, ed. F. Moseley, Occasional Publication No. 3, Yorkshire Geological Society, Leeds, pp. 121-45

McNamara, K. J. (1979). The age, stratigraphy and genesis of the Coniston Limestone Group in the southern Lake District. *Geol. J.*, **14**, 14-67

Mitchell, M., Taylor, B. J. and Ramsbottom, W. H. C. (1978). Carboniferous. In *The Geology of the Lake District*, ed. F. Moseley, Occasional Publication No. 3, Yorkshire Geological Society, Leeds, pp. 168-88

Moseley, F. (1968). Joints and other structures in the Silurian rocks of the southern Shap Fells, Westmorland. *Geol. J.*, **6**, 79-96

Moseley, F. (1972). A tectonic history of North-West England. *J. geol. Soc. Lond.*, **128**, 561-98

Moseley, F. (1983a). *The Volcanic Rocks of the Lake District*. Macmillan, London

Moseley, F. (1983b). Geological field mapping and photogeology. *Geology Teaching*, **8**, 82-7

Moseley, F. (1984). Lower Palaeozoic Lithostratigraphic Classification in the English Lake District. *Geol. J.*, **19**, 239-47

Moseley, F. and Ahmed, S. M. (1967). Carboniferous joints in the north of England and their relation to earlier and later structures. *Proc. Yorks. geol. Soc.*, **36**, 61-90

Moseley, F. and Millward, D. (1982). Ordovician volcanicity in the English Lake District. In *Igneous Rocks of the British Isles*, ed. D. Sutherland, Wiley, Chichester, pp. 93-111

Oliver, R. L. (1961). The Borrowdale volcanic and associated rocks of the Scafell area, English Lake District. *Q. Jl. geol. Soc. Lond.*, **117**, 377-417

Shackleton, E. H. (1968). *Lakeland Geology*. Dalesman, Clapham, North Yorkshire

Shackleton, E. H. (1975). *Geological Excursions in Lakeland*. Dalesman, Clapham, North Yorkshire

Soper, N. J. and Moseley, F. (1978). Structure. In *The Geology of the Lake District*, ed. F. Moseley, Occasional Publication No. 3, Yorkshire Geological Society, Leeds, pp. 45-67

Index